AT-SEA DISTRIBUTION AND ABUNDANCE OF SEABIRDS OFF SOUTHERN CALIFORNIA: A 20-YEAR COMPARISON

John W. Mason, Gerard J. McChesney, William R. McIver,
Harry R. Carter, John Y. Takekawa, Richard T. Golightly,
Joshua T. Ackerman, Dennis L. Orthmeyer, William M. Perry,
Julie L. Yee, Mark O. Pierson, and Michael D. McCrary

Studies in Avian Biology No. 33
A PUBLICATION OF THE COOPER ORNITHOLOGICAL SOCIETY

Cover painting (seabirds off southern California) by Sophie Webb

STUDIES IN AVIAN BIOLOGY

Edited by

Carl D. Marti
1310 East Jefferson Street
Boise, ID 83712

Spanish translation by
Cecilia Valencia

Studies in Avian Biology is a series of works too long for *The Condor*, published at irregular intervals by the Cooper Ornithological Society. Manuscripts for consideration should be submitted to the editor. Style and format should follow those of previous issues.

Price $15.00 including postage and handling. All orders cash in advance; make checks payable to Cooper Ornithological Society. Send orders to Cooper Ornithological Society, % Western Foundation of Vertebrate Zoology, 439 Calle San Pablo, Camarillo, CA 93010

ISBN: 9780943610726

Library of Congress Control Number: 2006939826
Printed at Cadmus Professional Communications, Ephrata, Pennsylvania 17522
Issued: 14 March 2007

CONTENTS

FIGURES

LIST OF AUTHORS

JOHN W. MASON
Department of Wildlife
Humboldt State University
Arcata, CA 95521

GERARD J. McCHESNEY
Department of Wildlife
Humboldt State University
Arcata, CA 95521
(Current address: USDI Fish and Wildlife Service,
San Francisco Bay National Wildlife Refuge,
PO Box 524, Newark, CA 94560)

WILLIAM R. McIVER
Department of Wildlife
Humboldt State University
Arcata, CA 95521
(Current address: USDI Fish and Wildlife Service,
2439 Portola Road, Suite B, Ventura, CA 93003)

HARRY R. CARTER
Department of Wildlife
Humboldt State University
Arcata, CA 95521
Current address: USDI Fish and Wildlife Service,
2439 Portola Road, Suite B, Ventura, CA 93003

JOHN Y. TAKEKAWA
U.S. Geological Survey
Western Ecological Research Center
San Francisco Bay Estuary Field Station
505 Azuar Drive
Vallejo, CA 94592

RICHARD T. GOLIGHTLY
Department of Wildlife
Humboldt State University
Arcata, CA 95521

JOSHUA T. ACKERMAN
U.S. Geological Survey, WERC
Davis Field Station
One Shields Avenue
University of California
Davis, CA 95616

DENNIS L. ORTHMEYER
U.S. Geological Survey, WERC
Dixon Field Station
6924 Tremont Road
Dixon, CA 95620
(Current address: Wildlife Services,
3419 A, Arden Way, Sacramento, CA 95825)

WILLIAM M. PERRY
U.S. Geological Survey, WERC
Dixon Field Station
6924 Tremont Road
Dixon, CA 95620

JULIE L. YEE
U.S. Geological Survey, WERC
3020 State University Drive East
Modoc Hall, Room 3006
Sacramento, CA 95819

MARK O. PIERSON
U.S. Minerals Management Service
Pacific Outer Continental Shelf Region
770 Paseo Camarillo
Camarillo, CA 93010
Deceased

MICHAEL D. McCRARY
U.S. Minerals Management Service
Pacific Outer Continental Shelf Region
770 Paseo Camarillo
Camarillo, CA 93010
(Current address: USDI Fish and Wildlife Service,
2439 Portola Road, Suite B, Ventura, CA 93003)

AT-SEA DISTRIBUTION AND ABUNDANCE OF SEABIRDS OFF SOUTHERN CALIFORNIA: A 20-YEAR COMPARISON

John W. Mason, Gerard J. McChesney, William R. McIver, Harry R. Carter, John Y. Takekawa, Richard T. Golightly, Joshua T. Ackerman, Dennis L. Orthmeyer, William M. Perry, Julie L. Yee, Mark O. Pierson, and Michael D. McCrary

Abstract. We conducted aerial at-sea and coastal surveys to examine the distribution and abundance of seabirds off southern California, from Cambria, California, to the Mexican border. From May 1999–January 2002, we flew 102 d, covered >54,640 km of transect lines, and conducted nine complete surveys of southern California in January, May, and September. We identified 54 species comprising 12 families and counted >135,000 individuals. Seabird densities were greater along island and mainland coastlines than at sea and were usually greatest in January surveys. Densities were greatest at sea near the northern Channel Islands in January and north of Point Conception in May, and lowest in the southwestern portion of the Southern California Bight in all survey months. On coastal transects, seabird densities were greatest along central and southern portions of the mainland coastline from Point Arguello to Mexico. We estimated that 981,000 ± 144,000 ($\overline{x}$ ± SE) seabirds occurred in the study area in January, 862,000 ± 95,000 in May, and 762,000 ± 72,000 in September. California Gulls (*Larus californicus*), Western Grebes (*Aechmophorus occidentalis*), and Cassin's Auklets (*Ptychoramphus aleuticus*) were most abundant in January surveys at sea, whereas Sooty and Short-tailed shearwaters (*Puffinus griseus* and *P. tenuirostris*), phalaropes (*Phalaropus* spp.), and Western Gulls (*Larus. occidentalis*) were most abundant in May and September surveys. On coastal transects, California Gulls, Western Grebes, Western Gulls, and Surf Scoters (*Melanitta perspicillata*) were most abundant in January; Western Grebes, Western Gulls, Surf Scoters, and Brown Pelicans (*Pelecanus occidentalis*) were most abundant in May; and Sooty Shearwaters, Short-tailed Shearwaters, Western Gulls, Western Grebes, Brown Pelicans, and Heermann's Gulls (*Larus heermanni*) were most abundant in September. Compared to historical seabird densities collected in the same area two decades ago (1975–1978 and 1980–1983), abundance was lower by 14% in January, 57% in May, and 42% in September. Common Murres (*Uria aalge*, ≥75% in each season), Sooty Shearwaters (55% in May, 27% in September), and Bonaparte's Gulls (*L. philadelphia*, ≥95% in each season) had lower densities. Conversely, Brown Pelicans (167% overall), Xantus's Murrelets (*Synthliboramphus hypoleucus*; 125% overall), Cassin's Auklets (100% overall), Ashy Storm-Petrels (*Oceanodroma homochroa*, 450% overall) and Western Gulls (55% in May), and Brandt's Cormorants (*Phalacrocorax penicillatus*, 450% in September) had greater densities. Our results indicate that seabird abundance has declined off the southern California coast in the past two decades, and these declines may be warning signs of environmental degradation in the region or effects of larger forces such as climate change.

Key Words: abundance, aerial surveys, density, distribution, seabirds, Southern California Bight.

DISTRIBUCIÓN Y ABUNDANCIA DE AVES MARINAS FUERA DEL MAR DE CALIFORNIA SUR: UNA COMPARACIÓN DE 20 AÑOS

Resumen. Condujimos muestreos aéreos en el mar y en la costa, con el fin de examinar la distribución y abundancia de aves marinas fuera del mar del sur de California, desde Cambria, California, hasta la frontera Mexicana. De mayo de 1999 a enero del 2002, volamos 102 d, cubriendo >54,640 km de líneas de transecto, y condujimos nueve muestreos completos del sur de California en enero, mayo, y septiembre. Identificamos 54 especies que comprenden 12 familias y contamos >135,000 individuos. Las densidades de aves marinas fueron mayores a lo largo de las líneas costeras de islas y del continente a aquellas del mar, y generalmente fueron mayores en los muestreos de enero. Las densidades fueron más grandes en el mar cerca del norte de las Islas Canal en enero y en el norte de Punto de Concepción en mayo, y las más bajas en la porción suroeste de Ensenada California Sur en todos los meses del muestreo. En los transectos de costa, las densidades de aves marinas fueron las más grandes a lo largo de las porciones central y sureña de la costa continental desde Punto Arguello hasta México. Estimamos que 981,000 ± 144,000 ($\overline{x}$ ± SE) aves marinas aparecieron en el área de estudio en enero, 862,000 ± 95,000 en mayo, y 762,000 ± 172,000 en septiembre. Las Gaviotas de California (*Larus californicus*), el Achichincle Pico-amarillo (*Aechmophorus occidentalis*), y la Alcuela Oscura (*Ptychoramphus aleuticus*) fueron más abundantes en los muestreos de enero en el mar, mientras que la Pardela Gris y la Pardela Colacorta (*Puffinus griseus* and *P. tenuirostris*), el falaropus (*Phalaropus* spp.), y la Gaviota Occidental (*Larus. occidentalis*) fueron más abundantes en los muestreos de mayo y septiembre. En los transectos de costa, las Gaviotas de California, Achichcles Pico-amarillo, Gaviotas Occidentales, y la Negreta Nuca-blanca (*Melanitta perspicillata*) fueron más abundantes en enero; Achichincles Pico-amarillo, Gaviotas Occidentales, Negretas Cola-blanca, y Pelícanos Pardo

1

(*Pelecanus occidentalis*) fueron más abundantes en mayo; la Pardela Gris, la Pardela Cola-corta, Gaviotas Occidentales, Pelícanos Pardo, y Gaviotas Ploma (*Larus heermanni*) fueron más abundantes en septiembre. Comparada a las densidades históricas de aves marítimas colectadas hace dos décadas (1975–1978 y 1980–1983), la abundancia fue más baja en un 14% en enero, 57% en mayo, y 42% en septiembre. El Arao Común (*Uria aalge*, ≥75% en cada estación), Pardelas Gris (55% en mayo, 27% en septiembre), y La Gaviota de Bonaparte (*L. philadelphia*, ≥95% en cada estación) tuvieron densidades más bajas. En cambio, los Pelicanos Pardo (167% total), el Mergulo de Xantos (*Synthliboramphus hypoleucus*; 125% total), la Arcuela Oscura (100% total), el Paiño Cenizo (*Oceanodroma homochroa*, 450% total) y las Gaviotas Occidentales (55% en mayo), y el Cormoran de Brandt (*Phalacrocorax penicillatus*, 450% en septiembre) tuvieron densidades mayores. Nuestros resultados indican que la abundancia de aves marinas ha declinado fuera de la costa de California Sur en las ultimas dos décadas, y dichas declinaciones quizás sean signos de alerta de degradación ambiental en la región o efectos de fuerzas mayores, tales como el cambio climático.

Ocean waters off southern California, and the Southern California Bight (SCB) in particular, comprise important habitat for numerous seabird species (Hunt et al. 1980, Briggs et al. 1987; Veit et al. 1996, 1997; Pierson et al. 2000; K. Briggs, unpubl. data; H. Carter, unpubl. data). More than 20 species of seabirds breed in southern California, almost entirely on the California Channel Islands (hereafter Channel Islands), including four threatened or endangered seabird species (USDI Fish and Wildlife Service 2002). The SCB is the only region in the U.S. supporting breeding Brown Pelicans (*Pelecanus occidentalis*), Black Storm-Petrels (*Oceanodroma melania*), Elegant Terns (*Thalasseus elegans*), and Xantus's Murrelets (*Synthliboramphus hypoleucus*; H. Carter, unpubl. data; Burness et al. 1999). The region also contains about half of the world population of Xantus's Murrelets and Ashy Storm-Petrels (*Oceanodroma homochroa*; Carter et al., in press; Karnovsky et al., in press; H. Carter, unpubl. data; E. Burkett, unpubl. data). In addition, numerous seabirds migrate through or winter in southern California (Briggs et al. 1987, Mason, unpubl. data).

The SCB is bordered by major metropolitan areas (Los Angeles, Santa Barbara, and San Diego). Approximately $9,000,000,000 are contributed annually to local economies via offshore oil production, oil transportation by tankers, commercial shipping, commercial fishing, military activities (weapons testing and exercises), and public recreation (Anderson et al. 1993, Carter et al. 2000, Carter et al. 2003, McCrary et al. 2003, USDI Fish and Wildlife Service 2005). From 1970–2000, human populations increased by 64% with concomitant increases in coastal development, sewage discharge, recreational use, and commercial activities (U.S. Census Bureau 2003). More than 16,000,000 people currently live in counties rimming the SCB (U.S. Census Bureau 2003). As a consequence, great concern exists regarding potential effects of human activities on seabird and marine mammal populations, and federal and state agencies have established the Channel Islands National Park, Channel Islands National Marine Sanctuary, and several smaller marine reserves to protect wildlife in this region.

In the past 20 yr, southern California also has undergone changes in physical and biological oceanography. An increase in sea-surface temperature (SST) coincident with the Pacific Decadal Oscillation (PDO) began in 1977 and extended to 1999. This period was characterized by reduced phytoplankton and zooplankton abundances and altered prey-fish distributions (Mantua et al. 1997, Minobe 1997, Peterson and Schwing 2003). The period from 1999–2002 was characterized by La Niña conditions very different from the preceding years with record-high upwelling values (1999), high primary productivity, and high seabird productivity (Peterson and Schwing 2003). Several studies in the 1980s and 1990s reported declines in abundance or changes in community composition of plankton and seabirds in the California Current System (CCS; Veit et al. 1996, 1997; McGowan et al. 1998, Oedekoven et al. 2001, Hyrenbach and Veit 2003). The CCS extends 1,000 km from southern British Columbia, Canada, to northwestern Baja California, Mexico, and consists of a southward surface current, a poleward undercurrent, and several surface countercurrents. A temperature increase of 0.8 C in the upper 500 m of the CCS occurred between 1950 and 1992, with most of the increase occurring since 1975 (Roemmich 1992). Reproductive success of seabirds generally declined as ocean temperatures increased off central California (Ainley and Boekelheide 1990; Ainley et al. 1994, 1996; Sydeman 2001).

In contrast, the effects of DDE (dichlorodiphenyldichloroethylene) contamination have abated in the SCB, leading to increased reproductive success of several seabird species including Brown Pelicans and cormorants (*Phalacrocorax* spp.; F. Gress, unpubl. data), although other species (e.g., storm-petrels) may still be affected (Carter et al., in press). Based on seabird surveys conducted in 1991, H. Carter (unpubl. data) reported increased populations of several species, including Brown Pelicans, cormorants, and Western Gulls (*Larus occidentalis*), but decreased populations of Cassin's Auklets (*Ptychoramphus aleuticus*) and Xantus's Murrelets compared with surveys conducted in the 1970s.

Collectively, these changes in oceanography and human activities prompted a need for updated information regarding at-sea populations of seabirds in southern California using techniques that would allow comparison with previous seabird surveys conducted by Briggs et al. (1987). In 1975–1978 and 1980–1983 (hereafter 1975–1983), Briggs et al. (1987) conducted the first replicated, quantitative assessment of the distribution, abundance, and diversity of seabirds off California using aerial-survey techniques. Surveys in the SCB were conducted from 1975–1978 and off central and northern California from 1980–1983. More than two decades later (1999–2002), we used similar aerial-survey techniques to provide updated information and examine trends in the at-sea

distribution and abundance of seabirds in southern California.

STUDY AREA

The study area encompassed continental-shelf and slope waters from 35° 35′ N (off the city of Cambria, San Luis Obispo County, California) south to 32° 32′ N (the Mexican border), and from the mainland shoreline west to 122° W at the northern boundary, and to 119° 30′ W at the southern boundary (Fig. 1). In this area, most of the coastline and seafloor are oriented north to south. Like most parts of the California coast, the continental shelf gradually slopes westward before dropping precipitously to depths >3,000 m. At Point Conception, the coastline and bottom topography abruptly turn eastward to southeastward and transition to a southward orientation between Los Angeles and San Diego.

For this study, we considered that the SCB extended from Point Conception to just south of the Mexican border. Off Point Conception and

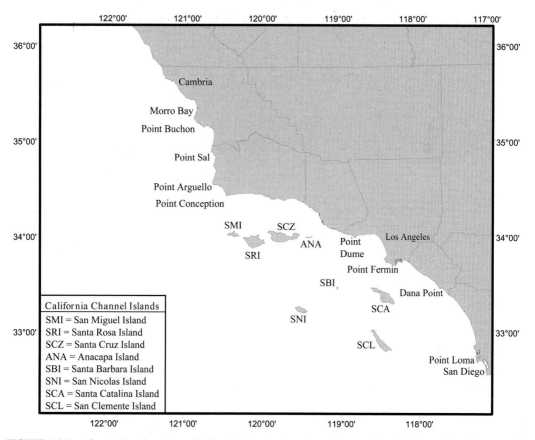

FIGURE 1. Map of central and southern California showing locations of county boundaries, major cities, coastal points, and islands.

to the north, shelf currents and water properties respond to strong, persistent upwelling-favorable winds, whereas in the SCB and offshore, flows consist of eddies, jets, and fronts which show no relation to local winds (Harms and Winant 1998). These unique conditions result in a transition zone between warmer subtropical waters to the south and colder nutrient-rich waters to the north (Hunt et al. 1980). As a result, the SCB and adjacent waters host a diverse avifauna that includes species typical of both temperate and tropical climates. Several seabird species have their northern or southern distribution limit in this region.

The SCB contains a variety of bathymetric and land features that combine to form a highly complex oceanographic region. Eight major islands, 11 deep-water basins, three major banks and seamounts, and at least 13 major submarine canyons bisect the SCB (Dailey et al. 1993, Hickey 1993). These features strongly affect local circulation patterns of the California

current, which turns from its more typical flow toward the equator to a flow toward the pole in the central-southern SCB, with a predominant counterclockwise eddy south of the northern Channel Islands (Hickey 1993). The strong coastal upwelling off the northern and central California coasts is much reduced in the southern portion of the SCB, resulting in warmer and less productive waters.

Human activities in southern California have affected seabirds. The southern California coast is one of the most densely populated coastal areas in the U.S. and this has led to highly modified coastal habitats. Various pollutants, including oil, sewage, agricultural runoff, pesticides, and other chemicals have affected coastal waters (Schiff 2000). Several offshore oil leases for commercial oil development are located off Point Conception and the Santa Barbara and San Pedro channels; several other lease sales remain undeveloped (Fig. 2). In southern California, four active offshore oil platforms exist off

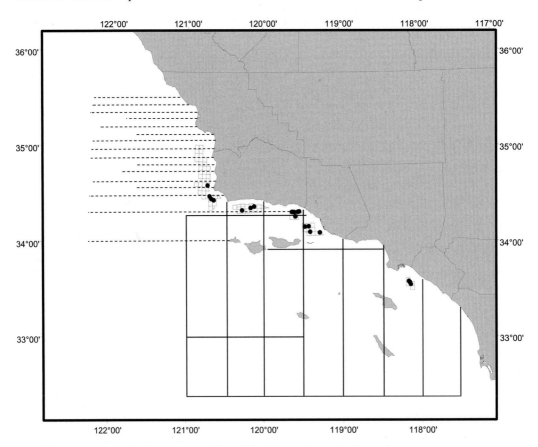

FIGURE 2. Map of central and southern California showing oil lease and platform locations and survey lines flown by Briggs et al. (1987). Oil leases are represented by squares. Platforms are represented by solid circles within lease areas. Lines surveyed in 1975–1978 are represented by solid lines. Lines surveyed in 1980–1983 are represented by dotted lines.

Point Conception and Point Arguello, 15 in the Santa Barbara Channel, and five in San Pedro Channel. Oil and gas operations are scheduled to continue on some of these platforms for more than a decade. Commercial ships, including oil tankers, pass through the area en route to and from SCB ports. Three major oil tanker and commercial ship transport lanes pass through the SCB to enter Los Angeles and Long Beach harbors, and significant tanker traffic and oil volume pass through the San Diego and Estero Bay-Avila Beach areas. Oil spills along the California, Oregon, and Washington coasts have resulted in significant losses to local seabird populations (Burger and Fry 1993, Carter 2003, USDI Fish and Wildlife Service 2005). The 1969 Santa Barbara oil spill in the northern SCB was the largest oil spill in the region and led to recognition of oil spill effects on seabirds (Carter 2003). Seabird mortality also has been documented for spills from offshore platforms, pipelines, onshore oil facilities, tankers, and military and commercial shipping (Anderson et al. 1993, Carter 2003). The region is used extensively by the military; in particular, the sea-test range of the Naval Air Systems Command covers a large portion of the southern California offshore zone. Additionally, several military bases are located along the mainland coast of southern California and on San Nicolas and San Clemente islands. Although little seabird mortality has been documented from military operations in southern California (i.e., missile and target-drone testing, low-level aircraft flights, and naval fleet maneuvers), seabirds may be disturbed during such activities (Carter et al. 2000).

METHODS

AERIAL SURVEY METHODOLOGY

Surveys were conducted from a high-winged, twin-engine Partenavia PN 68 Observer aircraft following methods developed for seabird observation by Briggs et al. (1985a, b; 1987). We flew surveys at 60 m above sea level at 160 km/hr ground speed and flew coastline (mainland and island) transects 300 m from shore. In ecologically sensitive areas (e.g., larger seabird nesting and roosting sites, and marine mammal rookery and haul-out sites), we flew 400 m from shore. Observers sat on each side of the aircraft and scanned the sea surface through bubble windows. Each observer counted and identified seabirds occurring within a 50-m strip on one side of the aircraft for a total strip width of 100 m when both observers were surveying simultaneously. At least one observer surveyed at all times, but individual effort was discontinued when glare obscured >25% of an observer's field of view. To ensure that we maintained a strip width of 50 m, we estimated sighting angles from the aircraft to the water using clinometers. Observers rechecked sighting angles with a clinometer several times during each survey.

Seabird observations were recorded on audiotape with hand-held tape recorders (VSC-2002, Model No. 14-1158, Tandy Corporation, Fort Worth, Texas). We used tape recorders instead of recording directly to computers (see dLog program below) because they recorded more quickly, especially for mixed-bird flocks, and provided a backup to the data. For each observation we recorded: species or nearest taxon, number of individuals (i.e., exact counts for small groups and estimated numbers for groups >10 birds), time to the nearest second, behavior (e.g., flying or sitting on water), and flight direction.

Each observer transcribed data from audiotapes onto standardized data forms and entered data into the computer program SIGHT (Micro Computer Solutions, Portland, OR) which had preset data entry protocols that helped to ensure accuracy. Two people checked data entry accuracy by comparing printed SIGHT data with hand-transcribed forms.

Location for each observation and tracked survey lines were determined using a Garmin® 12 Plus global positioning system (GPS; Garmin Ltd., Olathe, KS) connected to a laptop computer that was operated by a third observer. The program dLog (R. G. Ford Consulting, Portland, OR) recorded aircraft position (waypoint) from the GPS unit every 5 sec into a log file. We chose an interval of 5 sec to allow adequate spatial coverage of the trackline (225 m is traversed every 5 sec at our survey speed of 160 km/hr) and to limit the size of data files. We synchronized observer hand watches with the computer clock twice each survey day.

Following each survey, trackline log files were plotted in the geographical information system program ArcView (Version 3.3, ESRI, Redlands, CA) and checked for GPS errors or missing trackline data. For transects with missing trackline data (e.g., from occasional computer errors or momentary loss of satellite coverage), we created transect lines based on known waypoints and constant airspeed with interpolation programs written in the SAS statistics program (SAS Institute 1999). After correcting trackline files, we calculated the position of each sighting based on observation time with the program INTERPD (R. G. Ford Consulting, Portland, OR).

TRANSECT LOCATION DESIGN

Previous studies indicated greatest densities of seabirds in southern California occurred near the northern Channel Islands which include San Miguel, Santa Rosa, Santa Cruz, and Anacapa islands (hereafter the core area; Hunt et al. 1980; H. Carter, unpubl. data). Briggs et al. (1987) flew similar survey lines in this core area, and this also was the area of greatest offshore oil development in the study area (Fig. 2). Therefore, we designed transect lines to concentrate survey effort in the core area to account for spatial variation and obtain data on local breeders during the breeding season (Fig. 3). At-sea transects in the core area were oriented predominantly north-to-south (perpendicular to bathymetric contours) and were spaced at intervals of 10′ of longitude (~15 km). Outside the core area, transect lines were designed to survey the wide range of habitats and bathymetry changes throughout southern California. In order to cover a larger sampling area, at-sea transects outside

the core area were oriented east-to-west and spaced at intervals of 15′ of latitude (~27 km). Whereas all at-sea and coastal transect lines within the core area were replicated each survey month, transects outside the core area were surveyed only once per survey month. We conducted the replicate survey of the core area 5–10 days after the initial survey.

SURVEY TIMING DESIGN

A total of nine aerial surveys were conducted in January, May, and September, beginning in May 1999 and ending in January 2002. Fixed transect lines were located both at sea and along all mainland and island coastlines in southern California (Fig. 3). Coastal transects included the mainland shoreline from Cambria, California (35° 35′ N, 121° 07′ W) to the Mexican border (32° 32′ N, 117° 07′ W) and the shorelines of the eight major Channel Islands. January, May, and September were selected for survey months because these months usually coincide

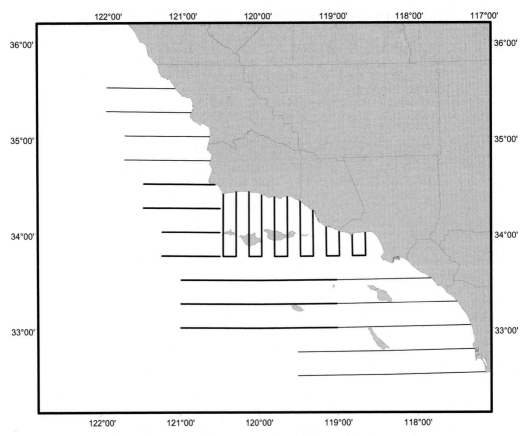

FIGURE 3. Map of central and southern California showing locations of core area and non-core area transect lines. Core area transect lines are represented by thicker lines. Non-core area transect lines are represented by thinner lines. The core area was surveyed twice each survey month from 1999–2002.

with over-wintering, breeding, and post-breeding dispersal, respectively, for many species of seabirds in southern California (K. Briggs, unpubl. data; Briggs et al. 1987; H. Carter, unpubl. data).

AT-SEA SUB-AREAS

We divided the at-sea study area into five sub-areas to facilitate comparison of our 1999–2002 and 1975–1983 data sets (Fig. 4). In general, these five sub-areas reflect major geographic regions in southern California, with differing oceanography and proximity to islands and the mainland. We also tried to make these similar in size and large enough for accurate density measurement for comparison of mean densities to each other. We positioned sub-area boundaries to bisect the distance between contiguous parallel transect lines (i.e., sub-area boundaries were equidistant from adjacent parallel transect lines). Briggs et al. (1987) surveyed farther offshore than we did; thus, we restricted statistical

comparisons to data collected only within our study area during both studies.

Sub-area 1 (S1) extended from Point Piedras Blancas to north of Point Conception and seaward 108 km. The southern boundary was along the edge of the transition zone between colder, up-welled waters of central California and the warmer waters of southern California (Chelton 1984, Lynn and Simpson 1987). This area represented the southern portion of the area surveyed by Briggs et al. (1987) in 1980–1983.

Sub-area 2 (S2) extended south from 34° 30′ N to 33° 40′ N and from 120° 30′ W seaward to the western edge of the study area 117 km west of San Miguel Island. This area represented the offshore zone west of the northern Channel Islands. It was downstream and slightly offshore from the central California upwelling zone and was largely outside the foraging areas for most Channel Islands seabirds during the breeding season.

Sub-area 3 (S3) comprised the area surrounding the northern Channel Islands from

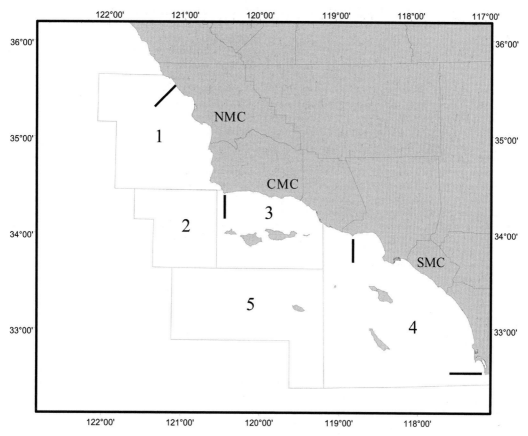

FIGURE 4. Map of central and southern California showing locations of at-sea and coastal subareas. At-sea sub-areas are numbered 1–5. Coastal sub-area boundaries are denoted by bars. NMC = northern mainland coast. CMC = central mainland coast. SMC = southern mainland coast.

Point Conception east to Point Mugu. Main ecological features of this area included the Santa Barbara Channel and the northern Channel Islands seabird-breeding habitat. Significant upwelling (Point Conception upwelling plume) from S1 becomes entrained in the western half of S3 (Denner et al. 1988, Harms and Winant 1998).

Sub-area 4 (S4) comprised the eastern SCB and was less influenced by coastal upwelling and had fewer breeding seabirds relative to S3 (H. Carter, unpubl. data). Sub-area four contained breeding and roosting habitat provided by Santa Barbara, Santa Catalina, and San Clemente islands and complex bathymetry with several deep basins and the Santa Rosa Ridge.

Sub-area 5 (S5) represented the offshore portion of the southwestern SCB and contained large expanses of open, deep ocean as well as ocean ridges and banks. The northern section of S5 was influenced by the Point Conception upwelling plume, but compared with S1, S2, and S3, waters were generally warmer, more saline, and less nutrient enriched (Harms and Winant 1998). San Nicolas Island provided breeding and roosting habitat in S5.

COASTAL SUB-AREAS

Coastal at-sea areas along the mainland and Channel Islands also were divided into five sub-areas—three mainland sub-areas and two island coastline sub-areas (Fig. 4). We created coastline sub-areas to represent biologically distinct regions and attempted to equalize transect length within each sub-area. Coastal sub-areas were not intended to match at-sea sub-areas because factors affecting abundance and distribution of avifauna on coastal and at-sea transects are known to differ for many reasons including different prey types, water masses, and use of roosting habitats (Briggs et al. 1987, Baird 1993).

Northern mainland coast (NMC) included the northern portion of the mainland coastline extending from Cambria to Point Arguello. The NMC was oceanographically similar to the central California coast and characterized by strong, upwelling-favorable winds. Coastlines are highly exposed and a mixture of rock and beach, with deep water close to shore.

Central mainland coast (CMC) included the central portion of the mainland coastline from Point Arguello to just east of Point Dume and included Point Conception, the northern Santa Barbara Channel coastline, and Mugu Lagoon. Coastlines are rocky until Santa Barbara then undergo transition to sandy beach, with a large, relatively shallow shelf off Ventura.

Southern mainland coast (SMC) included the southern portion of the mainland coastline just east of Point Dume to the Mexican border and included Santa Monica Bay, Palos Verdes, Dana Point, and Point Loma. Coastlines are mainly sandy beaches with moderate shelf.

Northern island coast (NIC) included the northern Channel Islands with mainly rocky coastlines, deep water close to shore, and large and small seabird colonies.

Southern island coast (SIC) included the southern Channel Islands (Santa Barbara, San Nicolas, Santa Catalina, and San Clemente islands). Coastlines are mainly rocky and include mainly small seabird colonies with deep water close to shore.

SPATIAL ANALYSIS METHODS

Trackline data files were used to generate point and line coverages in ArcInfo (ESRI, Redlands, CA). In order to estimate the areas surveyed for calculating seabird densities, we buffered the tracklines based upon the number of observers (50 m for one, 100 m for two). These buffered transects were then overlayed on the entire study area and divided into 1' × 1' and 5' × 5' latitude and longitude grid cells. Each transect section was labeled with a unique grid identifier. We separated strip transect data into coastal versus at-sea areas.

Observation points were then divided into these transect sections. Databases included seabird observations and the area surveyed within each grid cell at both 1' and 5' scales. These data were then analyzed with SAS programs to calculate species densities per cell. We originally collected data in geographic coordinates (NAD 27) and later re-projected data into the California Teale Albers projection to ensure accuracy of distance and area calculations. Track log GPS data collected during aerial surveys were reformatted with SAS programs to create formatted text files. We processed text files with an ArcInfo macro language program to create point and line coverages.

Seabird observations were linked to track log data, output as a dBASE file (dBASE Inc., Vestal, NY), imported into ArcView, and converted to shape files. We intersected shape files with buffered strips to transfer grid identifiers to points. These data were exported as dBASE files and analyzed with SAS programs to calculate densities.

STATISTICAL ANALYSES

Seabird distribution was examined hierarchically at three taxonomic levels: species, families, and all seabirds grouped together. Occasionally seabirds could be identified only to family or, very infrequently, only as unidentified species. The latter were excluded from species-specific analyses, but were used in the broader taxon groupings.

We analyzed at-sea and coastal-transect data separately and included both flying and non-flying birds in analyses. Unlike shipboard surveys, densities of flying birds were not corrected for the effect of flight direction (Spear and Ainley 1997). Because of the greater relative speed of the survey aircraft compared with flying seabirds, we assumed error in density calculations of flying birds to be negligible. We assessed differences among seasons (January, May, and September) and sub-areas. We compared our at-sea transect data with similar aerial-survey data collected in 1975–1978 throughout the SCB and in 1980–1983 off central California (Briggs et al. 1987). We were unable to compare coastal transect data because Briggs et al. (1987) did not conduct aerial coastal transects.

For the analysis of at-sea-transect data, mean densities and standard errors were calculated for each species separately for sub-area and season. Mean densities across grids were weighted by survey area within each grid. We estimated standard errors by the Taylor expansion method used in the SURVEYMEANS procedure in SAS. We used generalized linear mixed models (GLMM) to model species counts within grids (Poisson distribution) with means proportional to the area of buffered transect (offset variable; McCullagh and Nelder 1989) that varied according to sub-area, season, year, and replicate. Replicate variation was measured by comparing the two replicates of the survey route flown within the same month and year. We assessed effects of sub-area and season on densities and controlled for variation between replicates and years by including replicate and year as random effect variables in models.

We restricted the GLMM to test for differences in densities only for those sub-areas and seasons in which species were observed. For sub-areas or seasons in which a species was not observed, density and standard error were zero. In this case, one of two possibilities occurred: (1) the entire season or sub-area contained no individuals of a particular species causing season or sub-area to be significantly different from any other season or sub-area in which the species was observed at least once, or (2) the species was present but too rare to be observed with our survey techniques and effort. Because we had insufficient data for the GLMM to distinguish between these two alternatives, we simply identified sub-areas and seasons that

did not have observations and excluded these categories from statistical analysis.

For similar reasons, we occasionally restricted the GLMM to exclude the replicate random effect when no observations occurred for one of the replicates. Conversely, for species with suitably large densities, sufficient data were available to test for presence of sub-area and season interactions. All tests for sub-area, season, and interaction effects were conducted with F-statistics and considered to be statistically significant at the 0.05 alpha error level.

COMPARISONS TO PAST DENSITY ESTIMATES

We obtained data for Briggs et al. (1987) from (M. Bonnell, unpubl. data). Aerial survey data were collected in the SCB from 1975–1978 that corresponded to our areas S2–S5. Aerial survey data were also collected off central and northern California in 1980–1983 that corresponded to our area S1. We assigned observations from Briggs et al. (1987) to sub-areas based on latitude and longitude associated with each observation. To compare at-sea densities of seabirds between the two studies, we used Briggs et al. (1987) data that bracketed the months of our survey (i.e., observations from the December, January, and February 1975–1983 surveys were compared to our January observations; April, May, and June 1975–1983 were compared to May; and August, September, and October 1975–1983 were compared to September). We did this to account for variation in the timing of seasonal species density peaks in 1975–1983 and to ensure that, if Briggs et al. (1987) did not survey in January, May, or September in a particular year, that we could obtain data from a similar time of year. Unlike Briggs et al. (1987), we chose not to extrapolate at-sea densities to generate at-sea population estimates. Meaningful comparison of such estimates between surveys would be difficult because of the variation around estimates.

We excluded any random effects that were found to be insignificant sources of variation in the analysis of the 1999–2002 survey. If all random effects are removed from a GLMM, then the model simplifies into a generalized linear model (GLM). We used either the GLMM or GLM, depending on whether any random effects were present, to test differences in density between the 1975–1983 and 1999–2002 survey periods. We created a classification variable for both survey periods, which was included in the GLMM or GLM to test effects of period on density.

We compared survey periods separately for the five at-sea sub-areas. This allowed us to estimate period effects that might vary geographically without requiring sub-area to be a factor in the model. This also allowed us to avoid potential model convergence difficulties that might result from complex interaction terms, such as a three-way season by sub-area by period interaction. We retained season as a factor in the model and allowed a season and period interaction term whenever sufficient data existed to test it. We estimated the period effect across the entire sub-area by repeating the analysis using data pooled across all at-sea sub-areas. We used contrasts to express the difference in densities between survey periods averaged across seasons and Wald's Z-test to test the significance of this contrast.

DISTRIBUTION MAPS

We averaged seabird densities for 5′ grids across years and replicates for each survey month. This resulted in three maps for each species and family representing January, May, and September. To facilitate visual comparisons among maps for individual species or families, map legends were standardized for each species or family based on percentages of maximum densities observed for that species or family. The five categories were: (1) 0 (none observed), (2) >0–50% of densities, (3) >50–75% of densities, (4) >75–90% of densities, and (5) >90% of densities. Standardized density legends highlighted areas of greatest importance to individual species or families.

RESULTS

Between May 1999 and January 2002, we completed nine surveys of the entire area (102 flight days). For all surveys combined, we flew >54,600 km of transects with >20,100 km in the core area and >14,400 km along coastlines. We identified 54 species of seabirds representing 12 families and counted a total of 135,545 seabirds on transect.

Seabirds occurred in all sub-areas and in all seasons (Fig. 5). Densities (all species) averaged 33.7 birds/km^2 (for at-sea and coastal transects combined) and ranged from 0–12,244 birds/km^2. Densities for both at-sea and coastal transects were generally greatest in January (Tables 1–4), primarily due to large numbers of California Gulls (*Larus californicus*), Western Grebes (*Aechmophorus occidentalis*), Surf Scoters (*Melanitta perspicillata*) and, to a lesser extent, Black-legged Kittiwakes (*Rissa tridactyla*), Cassin's Auklets, loons, and phalaropes. In May, Western Grebes, Sooty Shearwaters (*Puffinus griseus*), phalaropes, and Western Gulls were the most abundant species in southern California. Sooty Shearwaters were the

most abundant seabird in September, followed by Western Grebes, Western Gulls, and Brown Pelicans. Maximum seabird densities for a single 5′ grid occurred in September, involving large flocks of Sooty Shearwaters.

In 1999-2002, mean monthly abundance of seabirds was 981,000 ± 144,000 in January, 862,000 ± 95,000 in May, and 762,000 ± 172,000 in September. Among five at-sea sub-areas, greatest seabird densities occurred in S3 in January and in S1 in May and September. Western Grebes, California and Western gulls, and Cassin's Auklets were the most abundant species in S3 in January. Sooty and Short-tailed shearwaters, phalaropes, and Cassin's Auklets were most abundant in S1 in May, and Sooty and Short-tailed shearwaters, phalaropes, Common or Arctic terns, and Pink-footed Shearwaters were the most abundant species in September.

Among five coastal sub-areas, densities were greater along mainland rather than island coasts because of large numbers of Western Grebes, Sooty and Short-tailed shearwaters, and Surf Scoters, and to a lesser extent, terns. Greatest coastal seabird densities were found in CMC in January and May and in NMC in September (Table 5). Western Grebes, California and Western gulls, and Surf Scoters were the most abundant species in CMC in January. Western Grebes, cormorants, Western Gulls, and Brown Pelicans were the most abundant species in CMC in May. Sooty Shearwaters, Heermann's and Western gulls, Brown Pelicans, and cormorants were the most abundant species in the NMC in September.

All estimates of mean at-sea densities are presented separately by species, season, and geographic sub-area (Tables 1a–e). Mean densities that were greatest along mainland coastlines, island coastlines, and both coastline types are presented separately by species and season (Tables 2a–c). Mean densities for each coastline sub-area are presented for mainland coastlines (Tables 3a–c) and island coastlines (Tables 4a, 4b), and statistical tests of variation are summarized for seasonal (Table 5) and geographic (Table 6) differences. Random effects for year and replicate were not found to be significant (P > 0.15 for all species), so we compared at-sea densities between 1975–1983 and 1999–2002 surveys using GLM (Tables 7a, 7b).

Densities for all seabirds combined differed among at-sea and coastal sub-areas. Greatest densities of seabirds occurred in S3 (Table 1c) and in NMC (Tables 2–4), whereas lowest densities occurred in S5 (Table 1e) and in SIC (Tables 2–4). Densities along at-sea transects did not differ consistently among seasons, but greatest seasonal densities for at-sea transects occurred

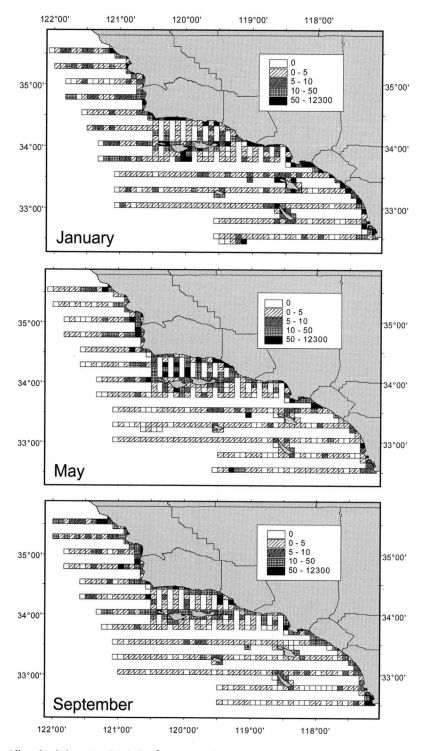

FIGURE 5. All seabird densities (birds/km²) and distribution off southern California from 1999–2002 during January, May, and September.

TABLE 1A. DENSITIES (BIRDS/KM² ± SE) OF SEABIRDS WITHIN AT-SEA SUB-AREA S1 (NORTH) DURING JANUARY, MAY, AND SEPTEMBER FROM 1999–2002.

Species		January	May	September
			S1 (North)	
All seabirds		9.57 ± 1.09	22.75 ± 5.76	19.37 ± 3.71
Loons	Gaviidae	0.24 ± 0.07	0.38 ± 0.22	0.01 ± 0.01
Common	Gavia immer	0.05 ± 0.02	0.00 ± 0.00	0.00 ± 0.00
Pacific	Gavia pacifica	0.14 ± 0.06	0.38 ± 0.22	0.00 ± 0.00
Red-throated	Gavia stellata	0.01 ± 0.01	0.00 ± 0.00	0.00 ± 0.00
Grebes	Podicipedidae	0.11 ± 0.06	0.03 ± 0.02	0.08 ± 0.05
Horned	Podiceps auritus	0.00 ± 0.00	0.00 ± 0.00	0.00 ± 0.00
Pied-billed	Podilymbus podiceps	0.00 ± 0.00	0.00 ± 0.00	0.00 ± 0.00
Western	Aechmophorus occidentalis	0.11 ± 0.06	0.03 ± 0.02	0.08 ± 0.05
Albatrosses	Diomedeidae	0.02 ± 0.01	0.03 ± 0.02	0.00 ± 0.00
Black-footed	Phoebastria nigripes	0.02 ± 0.01	0.03 ± 0.02	0.00 ± 0.00
Laysan	Phoebastria immutabilis	0.00 ± 0.00	0.00 ± 0.00	0.00 ± 0.00
Shearwaters and fulmars	Procellariidae	0.26 ± 0.06	8.56 ± 4.26	11.06 ± 3.49
Buller's Shearwater	Puffinus bulleri	0.00 ± 0.00	0.00 ± 0.00	0.04 ± 0.02
Black-vented Shearwater	Puffinus opisthomelas	0.02 ± 0.01	0.00 ± 0.00	0.14 ± 0.14
Northern Fulmar	Fulmarus glacialis	0.18 ± 0.05	0.13 ± 0.04	0.01 ± 0.01
Pink-footed Shearwater	Puffinus creatopus	0.03 ± 0.01	0.07 ± 0.03	1.06 ± 0.42
Sooty Shearwater	Puffinus griseus	0.03 ± 0.01	8.35 ± 4.26	9.78 ± 3.37
Storm-Petrels	Hydrobatidae	0.05 ± 0.03	0.06 ± 0.02	0.28 ± 0.13
Ashy	Oceanodroma homochroa	0.03 ± 0.02	0.05 ± 0.02	0.20 ± 0.13
Black	Oceanodroma melania	0.00 ± 0.00	0.00 ± 0.00	0.01 ± 0.01
Leach's	Oceanodroma leucorhoa	0.00 ± 0.00	0.00 ± 0.00	0.06 ± 0.02
Tropicbirds	Phaethontidae	0.00 ± 0.00	0.00 ± 0.00	0.00 ± 0.00
Red-billed	Phaethon aethereus	0.00 ± 0.00	0.00 ± 0.00	0.00 ± 0.00
Pelicans	Pelecanidae	0.33 ± 0.13	0.03 ± 0.03	0.01 ± 0.01
Brown	Pelecanus occidentalis	0.33 ± 0.13	0.03 ± 0.03	0.01 ± 0.01
Cormorants	Phalacrocoracidae	0.57 ± 0.37	0.04 ± 0.02	0.09 ± 0.04
Brandt's	Phalacrocorax penicillatus	0.08 ± 0.05	0.01 ± 0.01	0.01 ± 0.01
Double-crested	Phalacrocorax auritus	0.32 ± 0.30	0.00 ± 0.00	0.00 ± 0.00
Pelagic	Phalacrocorax pelagicus	0.00 ± 0.00	0.01 ± 0.01	0.01 ± 0.01
Sea ducks	Anatidae	0.10 ± 0.06	0.00 ± 0.00	0.00 ± 0.00
Brant	Branta bernicla	0.00 ± 0.00	0.00 ± 0.00	0.00 ± 0.00
Red-breasted Merganser	Mergus serrator	0.00 ± 0.00	0.00 ± 0.00	0.00 ± 0.00
Surf Scoter	Melanitta perspicillata	0.10 ± 0.06	0.00 ± 0.00	0.00 ± 0.00
White-winged Scoter	Melanitta fusca	0.00 ± 0.00	0.00 ± 0.00	0.00 ± 0.00

Table 1a. Continued.

Species		S1 (North)		
		January	May	September
Larids	Laridae			
Gulls	Larinae			
Black-legged Kittiwake	*Rissa tridactyla*	2.70 ± 0.37	2.29 ± 0.59	2.82 ± 0.65
Bonaparte's	*Larus philadelphia*	2.67 ± 0.37	2.10 ± 0.58	1.24 ± 0.23
California	*Larus californicus*	0.48 ± 0.13	0.04 ± 0.04	0.00 ± 0.00
Glaucous	*Larus hyperboreus*	0.01 ± 0.01	0.02 ± 0.01	0.00 ± 0.00
Glaucous-winged	*Larus glaucescens*	1.30 ± 0.26	0.38 ± 0.22	0.01 ± 0.01
Heermann's	*Larus heermanni*	0.01 ± 0.01	0.00 ± 0.00	0.00 ± 0.00
Herring	*Larus argentatus*	0.02 ± 0.01	0.00 ± 0.00	0.00 ± 0.00
Mew	*Larus canus*	0.11 ± 0.05	0.00 ± 0.00	0.09 ± 0.04
Ring-billed	*Larus delawarensis*	0.02 ± 0.01	0.00 ± 0.00	0.00 ± 0.00
Sabine's	*Xena sabini*	0.00 ± 0.00	0.00 ± 0.00	0.00 ± 0.00
Western	*Larus occidentalis*	0.00 ± 0.00	0.53 ± 0.13	0.54 ± 0.17
Terns	Sterninae	0.53 ± 0.13	0.96 ± 0.51	0.54 ± 0.12
Caspian	*Hydroprogne caspia*	0.00 ± 0.00	0.12 ± 0.05	1.44 ± 0.60
Common/Arctic	*Sterna hirundo/paradisaea*	0.00 ± 0.00	0.01 ± 0.01	0.00 ± 0.00
Elegant	*Thalasseus elegans*	0.00 ± 0.00	0.08 ± 0.04	1.34 ± 0.60
Elegant/Royal	*Thalasseus elegans/maximus*	0.00 ± 0.00	0.00 ± 0.00	0.07 ± 0.07
Forster's	*Sterna forsteri*	0.00 ± 0.00	0.00 ± 0.00	0.02 ± 0.02
Least	*Sterna antillarum*	0.00 ± 0.00	0.01 ± 0.01	0.00 ± 0.00
Royal	*Thalasseus maximus*	0.00 ± 0.00	0.00 ± 0.00	0.00 ± 0.00
Jaegers and skuas	Stercorariinae	0.00 ± 0.00	0.00 ± 0.00	0.00 ± 0.00
Long-tailed Jaeger	*Stercorarius longicaudus*	0.03 ± 0.02	0.07 ± 0.03	0.14 ± 0.03
Parasitic Jaegar	*Stercorarius parasiticus*	0.00 ± 0.00	0.00 ± 0.00	0.00 ± 0.00
Pomarine Jaeger	*Stercorarius pomarinus*	0.00 ± 0.00	0.00 ± 0.00	0.01 ± 0.01
South Polar Skua	*Stercorarius maccormicki*	0.03 ± 0.02	0.02 ± 0.01	0.03 ± 0.01
Alcids	Alcidae	0.00 ± 0.00	0.00 ± 0.00	0.01 ± 0.01
Cassin's Auklet	*Ptychoramphus aleuticus*	3.97 ± 0.62	1.70 ± 0.76	0.94 ± 0.20
Common Murre	*Uria aalge*	1.62 ± 0.30	1.46 ± 0.69	0.23 ± 0.09
Pigeon Guillemots	*Cepphus columba*	0.75 ± 0.35	0.01 ± 0.01	0.48 ± 0.16
Rhinoceros Auklet	*Cerorhinca monocerata*	0.00 ± 0.00	0.01 ± 0.01	0.00 ± 0.00
Xantus's Murrelet	*Synthliboramphus hypoleucus*	1.47 ± 0.29	0.06 ± 0.04	0.04 ± 0.03
Phalaropes	Phalaropodinae	0.00 ± 0.00	0.16 ± 0.07	0.04 ± 0.04
Red	*Phalaropus fulicarius*	1.20 ± 0.25	9.60 ± 2.80	4.03 ± 0.99
Red-necked	*Phalaropus lobatus*	0.46 ± 0.11	1.85 ± 1.60	0.41 ± 0.21
		0.01 ± 0.01	3.10 ± 1.19	0.56 ± 0.18

TABLE 1B. DENSITIES (BIRDS/KM² ± SE) OF SEABIRDS WITHIN AT-SEA SUB-AREA S2 (WEST-CENTRAL) DURING JANUARY, MAY, AND SEPTEMBER FROM 1999–2002.

Species		S2 (West-central)		
		January	May	September
All seabirds		9.52 ± 2.14	4.37 ± 0.81	7.21 ± 2.04
Loons	Gaviidae	0.00 ± 0.00	0.00 ± 0.00	0.00 ± 0.00
Common	Gavia immer	0.00 ± 0.00	0.00 ± 0.00	0.00 ± 0.00
Pacific	Gavia pacifica	0.00 ± 0.00	0.00 ± 0.00	0.00 ± 0.00
Red-throated	Gavia stellata	0.00 ± 0.00	0.00 ± 0.00	0.00 ± 0.00
Grebes	Podicipedidae	0.00 ± 0.00	0.00 ± 0.00	0.00 ± 0.00
Horned	Podiceps auritus	0.00 ± 0.00	0.00 ± 0.00	0.00 ± 0.00
Pied-billed	Podilymbus podiceps	0.00 ± 0.00	0.00 ± 0.00	0.00 ± 0.00
Western	Aechmophorus occidentalis	0.00 ± 0.00	0.00 ± 0.00	0.00 ± 0.00
Albatrosses	Diomedeidae	0.04 ± 0.03	0.01 ± 0.01	0.00 ± 0.00
Black-footed	Phoebastria nigripes	0.00 ± 0.00	0.01 ± 0.01	0.00 ± 0.00
Laysan	Phoebastria immutabilis	0.04 ± 0.03	0.00 ± 0.00	0.00 ± 0.00
Shearwaters and fulmars	Procellariidae	0.35 ± 0.08	0.56 ± 0.13	0.27 ± 0.11
Buller's Shearwater	Puffinus bulleri	0.00 ± 0.00	0.00 ± 0.00	0.09 ± 0.05
Black-vented Shearwater	Puffinus opisthomelas	0.00 ± 0.00	0.00 ± 0.00	0.00 ± 0.00
Northern Fulmar	Fulmarus glacialis	0.31 ± 0.08	0.10 ± 0.05	0.00 ± 0.00
Pink-footed Shearwater	Puffinus creatopus	0.04 ± 0.02	0.09 ± 0.03	0.10 ± 0.07
Sooty Shearwater	Puffinus griseus	0.00 ± 0.00	0.37 ± 0.12	0.08 ± 0.04
Storm-Petrels	Hydrobatidae	0.00 ± 0.00	0.32 ± 0.09	0.24 ± 0.07
Ashy	Oceanodroma homochroa	0.00 ± 0.00	0.22 ± 0.08	0.12 ± 0.05
Black	Oceanodroma melania	0.00 ± 0.00	0.00 ± 0.00	0.02 ± 0.02
Leach's	Oceanodroma leucorhoa	0.00 ± 0.00	0.10 ± 0.03	0.07 ± 0.03
Tropicbirds	Phaethontidae	0.00 ± 0.00	0.00 ± 0.00	0.00 ± 0.00
Red-billed	Phaethon aethereus	0.00 ± 0.00	0.00 ± 0.00	0.00 ± 0.00
Pelicans	Pelecanidae	0.01 ± 0.01	0.00 ± 0.00	0.00 ± 0.00
Brown	Pelecanus occidentalis	0.01 ± 0.01	0.00 ± 0.00	0.00 ± 0.00
Cormorants	Phalacrocoracidae	0.00 ± 0.00	0.00 ± 0.00	0.00 ± 0.00
Brandt's	Phalacrocorax penicillatus	0.00 ± 0.00	0.00 ± 0.00	0.00 ± 0.00
Double-crested	Phalacrocorax auritus	0.00 ± 0.00	0.00 ± 0.00	0.00 ± 0.00
Pelagic	Phalacrocorax pelagicus	0.00 ± 0.00	0.00 ± 0.00	0.00 ± 0.00
Sea ducks	Anatidae	0.00 ± 0.00	0.00 ± 0.00	0.00 ± 0.00
Brant	Branta bernicla	0.00 ± 0.00	0.00 ± 0.00	0.00 ± 0.00
Red-breasted Merganser	Mergus serrator	0.00 ± 0.00	0.00 ± 0.00	0.00 ± 0.00
Surf Scoter	Melanitta perspicillata	0.00 ± 0.00	0.00 ± 0.00	0.00 ± 0.00
White-winged Scoter	Melanitta fusca	0.00 ± 0.00	0.00 ± 0.00	0.00 ± 0.00

Table 1b. Continued.

Species		S2 (West-central)		
		January	May	September
Larids	Laridae			
Gulls	Larinae	1.00 ± 0.15	0.73 ± 0.22	1.01 ± 0.20
Black-legged Kittiwake	*Rissa tridactyla*	0.98 ± 0.15	0.52 ± 0.15	0.24 ± 0.07
Bonaparte's	*Larus philadelphia*	0.58 ± 0.12	0.00 ± 0.00	0.00 ± 0.00
California	*Larus californicus*	0.00 ± 0.00	0.01 ± 0.01	0.00 ± 0.00
Glaucous	*Larus hyperboreus*	0.16 ± 0.07	0.00 ± 0.00	0.00 ± 0.00
Glaucous-winged	*Larus glaucescens*	0.00 ± 0.00	0.00 ± 0.00	0.00 ± 0.00
Heermann's	*Larus heermanni*	0.01 ± 0.01	0.00 ± 0.00	0.00 ± 0.00
Herring	*Larus argentatus*	0.00 ± 0.00	0.00 ± 0.00	0.00 ± 0.00
Mew	*Larus canus*	0.00 ± 0.00	0.00 ± 0.00	0.00 ± 0.00
Ring-billed	*Larus delawarensis*	0.00 ± 0.00	0.00 ± 0.00	0.00 ± 0.00
Sabine's	*Xema sabini*	0.00 ± 0.00	0.00 ± 0.00	0.00 ± 0.00
Western	*Larus occidentalis*	0.14 ± 0.06	0.30 ± 0.13	0.15 ± 0.06
Terns	Sterninae	0.00 ± 0.00	0.20 ± 0.06	0.06 ± 0.03
Caspian	*Hydroprogne caspia*	0.00 ± 0.00	0.21 ± 0.12	0.50 ± 0.13
Common/Arctic	*Sterna hirundo/paradisaea*	0.00 ± 0.00	0.00 ± 0.00	0.00 ± 0.00
Elegant	*Thalasseus elegans*	0.00 ± 0.00	0.21 ± 0.12	0.50 ± 0.13
Elegant/Royal	*Thalasseus elegans/maximus*	0.00 ± 0.00	0.00 ± 0.00	0.00 ± 0.00
Forster's	*Sterna forsteri*	0.00 ± 0.00	0.00 ± 0.00	0.00 ± 0.00
Least	*Sterna antillarum*	0.00 ± 0.00	0.00 ± 0.00	0.00 ± 0.00
Royal	*Thalasseus maximus*	0.00 ± 0.00	0.00 ± 0.00	0.00 ± 0.00
Jaegers and skuas	Stercorariinae	0.01 ± 0.01	0.00 ± 0.00	0.27 ± 0.10
Long-tailed Jaeger	*Stercorarius longicaudus*	0.00 ± 0.00	0.00 ± 0.00	0.00 ± 0.00
Parasitic Jaeger	*Stercorarius parasiticus*	0.00 ± 0.00	0.00 ± 0.00	0.02 ± 0.02
Pomarine Jaeger	*Stercorarius pomarinus*	0.01 ± 0.01	0.00 ± 0.00	0.07 ± 0.03
South Polar Skua	*Stercorarius maccormicki*	0.00 ± 0.00	0.00 ± 0.00	0.00 ± 0.00
Alcids	Alcidae	6.99 ± 2.15	0.13 ± 0.05	0.11 ± 0.07
Cassin's Auklet	*Ptychoramphus aleuticus*	6.59 ± 2.14	0.10 ± 0.04	0.03 ± 0.03
Common Murre	*Uria aalge*	0.00 ± 0.00	0.00 ± 0.00	0.00 ± 0.00
Pigeon Guillemots	*Cepphus columba*	0.00 ± 0.00	0.00 ± 0.00	0.00 ± 0.00
Rhinoceros Auklet	*Cerorhinca monocerata*	0.16 ± 0.05	0.01 ± 0.01	0.00 ± 0.00
Xantus's Murrelet	*Synthliboramphus hypoleucus*	0.07 ± 0.03	0.03 ± 0.02	0.00 ± 0.00
Phalaropes	Phalaropodinae	1.10 ± 0.22	2.61 ± 0.73	5.57 ± 1.94
Red	*Phalaropus fulicarius*	0.72 ± 0.19	0.13 ± 0.07	0.17 ± 0.05
Red-necked	*Phalaropus lobatus*	0.01 ± 0.01	0.91 ± 0.28	0.12 ± 0.07

TABLE 1C. DENSITIES (BIRDS/KM² ± SE) OF SEABIRDS WITHIN AT-SEA SUB-AREA S3 (CENTRAL) DURING JANUARY, MAY, AND SEPTEMBER FROM 1999–2002.

Species		S3 (Central)		
		January	May	September
All seabirds		23.69 ± 5.97	20.78 ± 3.56	17.87 ± 7.91
Loons	Gaviidae	1.45 ± 0.52	0.14 ± 0.06	0.00 ± 0.00
Common	Gavia immer	0.05 ± 0.02	0.00 ± 0.00	0.00 ± 0.00
Pacific	Gavia pacifica	0.88 ± 0.37	0.09 ± 0.04	0.00 ± 0.00
Red-throated	Gavia stellata	0.00 ± 0.00	0.00 ± 0.00	0.00 ± 0.00
Grebes	Podicipedidae	8.70 ± 4.91	0.30 ± 0.12	0.06 ± 0.05
Horned	Podiceps auritus	0.00 ± 0.00	0.00 ± 0.00	0.00 ± 0.00
Pied-billed	Podilymbus podiceps	0.00 ± 0.00	0.00 ± 0.00	0.00 ± 0.00
Western	Aechmophorus occidentalis	8.70 ± 4.91	0.30 ± 0.12	0.06 ± 0.05
Albatrosses	Diomedeidae	0.00 ± 0.00	0.00 ± 0.00	0.00 ± 0.00
Black-footed	Phoebastria nigripes	0.00 ± 0.00	0.00 ± 0.00	0.00 ± 0.00
Laysan	Phoebastria immutabilis	0.00 ± 0.00	0.00 ± 0.00	0.00 ± 0.00
Shearwaters and fulmars	Procellariidae	0.59 ± 0.19	9.99 ± 2.38	6.65 ± 3.00
Buller's Shearwater	Puffinus bulleri	0.00 ± 0.00	0.00 ± 0.00	0.05 ± 0.01
Black-vented Shearwater	Puffinus opisthomelas	0.08 ± 0.04	0.00 ± 0.00	0.14 ± 0.07
Northern Fulmar	Fulmarus glacialis	0.25 ± 0.07	0.05 ± 0.01	0.02 ± 0.01
Pink-footed Shearwater	Puffinus creatopus	0.03 ± 0.02	0.11 ± 0.03	1.11 ± 0.61
Sooty Shearwater	Puffinus griseus	0.05 ± 0.02	9.81 ± 2.37	3.34 ± 1.84
Storm-Petrels	Hydrobatidae	0.00 ± 0.00	0.04 ± 0.01	0.19 ± 0.05
Ashy	Oceanodroma homochroa	0.00 ± 0.00	0.02 ± 0.01	0.09 ± 0.03
Black	Oceanodroma melania	0.00 ± 0.00	0.02 ± 0.01	0.03 ± 0.02
Leach's	Oceanodroma leucorhoa	0.00 ± 0.00	0.00 ± 0.00	0.03 ± 0.02
Tropicbirds	Phaethontidae	0.00 ± 0.00	0.00 ± 0.00	0.00 ± 0.00
Red-billed	Phaethon aethereus	0.00 ± 0.00	0.00 ± 0.00	0.00 ± 0.00
Pelicans	Pelecanidae	0.24 ± 0.05	0.18 ± 0.04	2.96 ± 2.28
Brown	Pelecanus occidentalis	0.24 ± 0.05	0.18 ± 0.04	2.96 ± 2.28
Cormorants	Phalacrocoracidae	0.29 ± 0.06	0.30 ± 0.07	0.32 ± 0.11
Brandt's	Phalacrocorax penicillatus	0.14 ± 0.03	0.21 ± 0.05	0.21 ± 0.10
Double-crested	Phalacrocorax auritus	0.02 ± 0.01	0.03 ± 0.02	0.04 ± 0.01
Pelagic	Phalacrocorax pelagicus	0.01 ± 0.00	0.02 ± 0.01	0.00 ± 0.00
Sea ducks	Anatidae	0.38 ± 0.14	0.00 ± 0.00	0.00 ± 0.00
Brant	Branta bernicla	0.00 ± 0.00	0.00 ± 0.00	0.00 ± 0.00
Red-breasted Merganser	Mergus serrator	0.00 ± 0.00	0.00 ± 0.00	0.00 ± 0.00
Surf Scoter	Melanitta perspicillata	0.38 ± 0.14	0.00 ± 0.00	0.00 ± 0.00
White-winged Scoter	Melanitta fusca	0.00 ± 0.00	0.00 ± 0.00	0.00 ± 0.00

TABLE 1C. CONTINUED.

Species		S3 (Central)		
		September	May	January
Larids	Laridae	6.83 ± 2.93	2.56 ± 0.54	9.02 ± 2.26
Gulls	Larinae	6.48 ± 2.92	2.42 ± 0.54	8.96 ± 2.26
Black-legged Kittiwake	*Rissa tridactyla*	0.00 ± 0.00	0.00 ± 0.00	0.36 ± 0.08
Bonaparte's	*Larus philadelphia*	0.00 ± 0.00	0.00 ± 0.00	0.01 ± 0.00
California	*Larus californicus*	0.03 ± 0.01	0.09 ± 0.03	5.47 ± 2.17
Glaucous	*Larus hyperboreus*	0.00 ± 0.00	0.00 ± 0.00	0.00 ± 0.00
Glaucous-winged	*Larus glaucescens*	0.00 ± 0.00	0.00 ± 0.00	0.01 ± 0.00
Heermann's	*Larus heermanni*	0.13 ± 0.04	0.00 ± 0.00	0.72 ± 0.27
Herring	*Larus argentatus*	0.00 ± 0.00	0.00 ± 0.00	0.00 ± 0.00
Mew	*Larus canus*	0.00 ± 0.00	0.00 ± 0.00	0.00 ± 0.00
Ring-billed	*Larus delawarensis*	0.00 ± 0.00	0.00 ± 0.00	0.00 ± 0.00
Sabine's	*Xema sabini*	0.03 ± 0.02	0.05 ± 0.02	0.00 ± 0.00
Western	*Larus occidentalis*	5.83 ± 2.68	2.20 ± 0.54	2.11 ± 0.27
Terns	Sterninae	0.23 ± 0.07	0.12 ± 0.05	0.03 ± 0.01
Caspian	*Hydroprogne caspia*	0.01 ± 0.01	0.00 ± 0.00	0.02 ± 0.01
Common/Arctic	*Sterna hirundo/paradisaea*	0.09 ± 0.03	0.02 ± 0.01	0.00 ± 0.00
Elegant	*Thalasseus elegans*	0.01 ± 0.01	0.00 ± 0.00	0.00 ± 0.00
Elegant/Royal	*Thalasseus elegans/maximus*	0.06 ± 0.04	0.05 ± 0.04	0.01 ± 0.01
Forster's	*Sterna forsteri*	0.03 ± 0.02	0.02 ± 0.01	0.00 ± 0.00
Least	*Sterna antillarum*	0.00 ± 0.00	0.02 ± 0.01	0.00 ± 0.00
Royal	*Thalasseus maximus*	0.00 ± 0.00	0.00 ± 0.00	0.00 ± 0.00
Jaegers and skuas	Stercorariinae	0.11 ± 0.02	0.02 ± 0.01	0.03 ± 0.01
Long-tailed Jaeger	*Stercorarius longicaudus*	0.00 ± 0.00	0.00 ± 0.00	0.00 ± 0.00
Parasitic Jaegar	*Stercorarius parasiticus*	0.00 ± 0.00	0.00 ± 0.00	0.00 ± 0.00
Pomarine Jaeger	*Stercorarius pomarinus*	0.04 ± 0.01	0.00 ± 0.00	0.02 ± 0.01
South Polar Skua	*Stercorarius maccormicki*	0.00 ± 0.00	0.00 ± 0.00	0.00 ± 0.00
Alcids	Alcidae	0.20 ± 0.07	3.13 ± 1.63	2.31 ± 0.31
Cassin's Auklet	*Ptychoramphus aleuticus*	0.09 ± 0.04	2.75 ± 1.62	1.66 ± 0.29
Common Murre	*Uria aalge*	0.00 ± 0.00	0.07 ± 0.04	0.08 ± 0.03
Pigeon Guillemots	*Cepphus columba*	0.00 ± 0.00	0.02 ± 0.01	0.00 ± 0.00
Rhinoceros Auklet	*Cerorhinca monocerata*	0.01 ± 0.01	0.04 ± 0.02	0.46 ± 0.07
Xantus's Murrelet	*Synthliboramphus hypoleucus*	0.00 ± 0.00	0.22 ± 0.05	0.01 ± 0.01
Phalaropes	Phalaropodinae	0.65 ± 0.16	4.10 ± 1.05	0.57 ± 0.16
Red	*Phalaropus fulicarius*	0.03 ± 0.02	0.11 ± 0.07	0.27 ± 0.10
Red-necked	*Phalaropus lobatus*	0.08 ± 0.02	1.45 ± 0.50	0.03 ± 0.02

TABLE 1D. DENSITIES (BIRDS/KM^2 ± SE) OF SEABIRDS WITHIN AT-SEA SUB-AREA S4 (SOUTH-EAST) DURING JANUARY, MAY, AND SEPTEMBER FROM 1999–2002.

Species		S4 (South-east)		
		January	May	September
All seabirds		9.81 ± 1.74	5.92 ± 1.20	4.57 ± 0.69
Loons	Gaviidae	0.18 ± 0.09	0.00 ± 0.00	0.00 ± 0.00
Common	Gavia immer	0.00 ± 0.00	0.00 ± 0.00	0.00 ± 0.00
Pacific	Gavia pacifica	0.17 ± 0.09	0.00 ± 0.00	0.00 ± 0.00
Red-throated	Gavia stellata	0.00 ± 0.00	0.00 ± 0.00	0.00 ± 0.00
Grebes	Podicipedidae	0.13 ± 0.08	0.16 ± 0.12	0.02 ± 0.02
Horned	Podiceps auritus	0.00 ± 0.00	0.00 ± 0.00	0.00 ± 0.00
Pied-billed	Podilymbus podiceps	0.00 ± 0.00	0.00 ± 0.00	0.00 ± 0.00
Western	Aechmophorus occidentalis	0.13 ± 0.08	0.16 ± 0.12	0.02 ± 0.02
Albatrosses	Diomedeidae	0.00 ± 0.00	0.00 ± 0.00	0.00 ± 0.00
Black-footed	Phoebastria nigripes	0.00 ± 0.00	0.00 ± 0.00	0.00 ± 0.00
Laysan	Phoebastria immutabilis	0.00 ± 0.00	0.00 ± 0.00	0.00 ± 0.00
Shearwaters and fulmars	Procellariidae	0.81 ± 0.51	2.29 ± 0.33	1.79 ± 0.48
Buller's Shearwater	Puffinus bulleri	0.00 ± 0.00	0.00 ± 0.00	0.07 ± 0.06
Black-vented Shearwater	Puffinus opisthomelas	0.63 ± 0.51	0.00 ± 0.00	0.02 ± 0.01
Northern Fulmar	Fulmarus glacialis	0.09 ± 0.02	0.00 ± 0.00	0.01 ± 0.01
Pink-footed Shearwater	Puffinus creatopus	0.01 ± 0.01	0.12 ± 0.03	1.34 ± 0.44
Sooty Shearwater	Puffinus griseus	0.05 ± 0.02	2.02 ± 0.32	0.36 ± 0.12
Storm-Petrels	Hydrobatidae	0.02 ± 0.01	0.08 ± 0.03	0.18 ± 0.08
Ashy	Oceanodroma homochroa	0.00 ± 0.00	0.01 ± 0.01	0.10 ± 0.05
Black	Oceanodroma melania	0.00 ± 0.00	0.07 ± 0.02	0.04 ± 0.02
Leach's	Oceanodroma leucorhoa	0.00 ± 0.00	0.00 ± 0.00	0.02 ± 0.01
Tropicbirds	Phaethontidae	0.00 ± 0.00	0.00 ± 0.00	0.03 ± 0.01
Red-billed	Phaethon aethereus	0.00 ± 0.00	0.00 ± 0.00	0.01 ± 0.01
Pelicans	Pelecanidae	0.16 ± 0.06	0.11 ± 0.03	0.08 ± 0.03
Brown	Pelecanus occidentalis	0.16 ± 0.06	0.11 ± 0.03	0.08 ± 0.03
Cormorants	Phalacrocoracidae	0.05 ± 0.03	0.02 ± 0.01	0.02 ± 0.01
Brandt's	Phalacrocorax penicillatus	0.03 ± 0.02	0.01 ± 0.01	0.01 ± 0.01
Double-crested	Phalacrocorax auritus	0.00 ± 0.00	0.01 ± 0.01	0.00 ± 0.00
Pelagic	Phalacrocorax pelagicus	0.00 ± 0.00	0.00 ± 0.00	0.00 ± 0.00
Sea ducks	Anatidae	0.00 ± 0.00	0.00 ± 0.00	0.00 ± 0.00
Brant	Branta bernicla	0.00 ± 0.00	0.00 ± 0.00	0.00 ± 0.00
Red-breasted Merganser	Mergus serrator	0.00 ± 0.00	0.00 ± 0.00	0.00 ± 0.00
Surf Scoter	Melanitta perspicillata	0.00 ± 0.00	0.00 ± 0.00	0.00 ± 0.00
White-winged Scoter	Melanitta fusca	0.00 ± 0.00	0.00 ± 0.00	0.00 ± 0.00

TABLE 1D. CONTINUED.

Species		S4 (South-east)		
		January	May	September
Larids	Laridae	6.94 ± 1.59	1.61 ± 0.51	1.78 ± 0.35
Gulls	Larinae	6.87 ± 1.59	1.35 ± 0.51	1.38 ± 0.33
Black-legged Kittiwake	*Rissa tridactyla*	0.35 ± 0.15	0.00 ± 0.00	0.00 ± 0.00
Bonaparte's	*Larus philadelphia*	0.23 ± 0.07	0.10 ± 0.06	0.00 ± 0.00
California	*Larus californicus*	4.66 ± 1.53	0.36 ± 0.35	0.01 ± 0.01
Glaucous	*Larus hyperboreus*	0.00 ± 0.00	0.00 ± 0.00	0.00 ± 0.00
Glaucous-winged	*Larus glaucescens*	0.00 ± 0.00	0.00 ± 0.00	0.00 ± 0.00
Heermann's	*Larus heermanni*	0.06 ± 0.03	0.00 ± 0.00	0.06 ± 0.02
Herring	*Larus argentatus*	0.00 ± 0.00	0.00 ± 0.00	0.00 ± 0.00
Mew	*Larus canus*	0.00 ± 0.00	0.00 ± 0.00	0.00 ± 0.00
Ring-billed	*Larus delawarensis*	0.01 ± 0.01	0.00 ± 0.00	0.00 ± 0.00
Sabine's	*Xema sabini*	0.00 ± 0.00	0.04 ± 0.03	0.01 ± 0.01
Western	*Larus occidentalis*	1.08 ± 0.15	0.82 ± 0.19	1.20 ± 0.32
Terns	Sterninae	0.03 ± 0.01	0.25 ± 0.05	0.23 ± 0.05
Caspian	*Hydroprogne caspia*	0.00 ± 0.00	0.02 ± 0.01	0.00 ± 0.00
Common/Arctic	*Sterna hirundo/paradisaea*	0.00 ± 0.00	0.02 ± 0.01	0.11 ± 0.03
Elegant	*Thalasseus elegans*	0.00 ± 0.00	0.02 ± 0.01	0.01 ± 0.01
Elegant/Royal	*Thalasseus elegans/maximus*	0.01 ± 0.01	0.05 ± 0.02	0.07 ± 0.03
Forster's	*Sterna forsteri*	0.00 ± 0.00	0.02 ± 0.01	0.00 ± 0.00
Least	*Sterna antillarum*	0.00 ± 0.00	0.06 ± 0.02	0.00 ± 0.00
Royal	*Thalasseus maximus*	0.00 ± 0.00	0.00 ± 0.00	0.02 ± 0.02
Jaegers and skuas	Stercorariinae	0.04 ± 0.01	0.02 ± 0.01	0.16 ± 0.03
Long-tailed Jaeger	*Stercorarius longicaudus*	0.00 ± 0.00	0.00 ± 0.00	0.00 ± 0.00
Parasitic Jaegar	*Stercorarius parasiticus*	0.01 ± 0.01	0.00 ± 0.00	0.01 ± 0.01
Pomarine Jaeger	*Stercorarius pomarinus*	0.02 ± 0.01	0.02 ± 0.01	0.08 ± 0.03
South Polar Skua	*Stercorarius maccormicki*	0.00 ± 0.00	0.00 ± 0.00	0.00 ± 0.00
Alcids	Alcidae	1.02 ± 0.15	0.27 ± 0.15	0.02 ± 0.01
Cassin's Auklet	*Ptychoramphus aleuticus*	0.24 ± 0.07	0.05 ± 0.03	0.01 ± 0.01
Common Murre	*Uria aalge*	0.05 ± 0.02	0.00 ± 0.00	0.00 ± 0.00
Pigeon Guillemots	*Cepphus columba*	0.00 ± 0.00	0.00 ± 0.00	0.00 ± 0.00
Rhinoceros Auklet	*Cerorhinca monocerata*	0.60 ± 0.13	0.00 ± 0.00	0.00 ± 0.00
Xantus's Murrelet	*Synthliboramphus hypoleucus*	0.00 ± 0.00	0.22 ± 0.13	0.00 ± 0.00
Phalaropes	Phalaropodinae	0.45 ± 0.10	1.33 ± 1.00	0.65 ± 0.29
Red	*Phalaropus fulicarius*	0.33 ± 0.09	0.01 ± 0.01	0.02 ± 0.01
Red-necked	*Phalaropus lobatus*	0.02 ± 0.01	0.14 ± 0.06	0.12 ± 0.08

TABLE 1E. DENSITIES (BIRDS/KM² ± SE) OF SEABIRDS WITHIN AT-SEA SUB-AREA S5 (SOUTH) DURING JANUARY, MAY, AND SEPTEMBER FROM 1999–2002.

Species		S5 (South)		
		January	May	September
All seabirds		5.12 ± 0.38	5.26 ± 1.47	2.53 ± 0.29
Loons	Gaviidae	0.01 ± 0.01	0.00 ± 0.00	0.00 ± 0.00
Common	Gavia immer	0.00 ± 0.00	0.00 ± 0.00	0.00 ± 0.00
Pacific	Gavia pacifica	0.01 ± 0.01	0.00 ± 0.00	0.00 ± 0.00
Red-throated	Gavia stellata	0.00 ± 0.00	0.00 ± 0.00	0.00 ± 0.00
Grebes	Podicipedidae	0.00 ± 0.00	0.00 ± 0.00	0.00 ± 0.00
Horned	Podiceps auritus	0.00 ± 0.00	0.00 ± 0.00	0.00 ± 0.00
Pied-billed	Podilymbus podiceps	0.00 ± 0.00	0.00 ± 0.00	0.00 ± 0.00
Western	Aechmophorus occidentalis	0.00 ± 0.00	0.00 ± 0.00	0.00 ± 0.00
Albatrosses	Diomedeidae	0.00 ± 0.00	0.00 ± 0.00	0.00 ± 0.00
Black-footed	Phoebastria nigripes	0.00 ± 0.00	0.00 ± 0.00	0.00 ± 0.00
Laysan	Phoebastria immutabilis	0.00 ± 0.00	0.00 ± 0.00	0.00 ± 0.00
Shearwaters and fulmars	Procellariidae	0.33 ± 0.05	2.96 ± 1.45	0.36 ± 0.10
Buller's Shearwater	Puffinus bulleri	0.00 ± 0.00	0.00 ± 0.00	0.11 ± 0.06
Black-vented Shearwater	Puffinus opisthomelas	0.00 ± 0.00	0.00 ± 0.00	0.01 ± 0.01
Northern Fulmar	Fulmarus glacialis	0.29 ± 0.05	0.05 ± 0.02	0.01 ± 0.01
Pink-footed Shearwater	Puffinus creatopus	0.01 ± 0.01	0.04 ± 0.01	0.10 ± 0.03
Sooty Shearwater	Puffinus griseus	0.02 ± 0.01	2.85 ± 1.45	0.13 ± 0.07
Storm-Petrels	Hydrobatidae	0.26 ± 0.06	0.55 ± 0.08	0.29 ± 0.04
Ashy	Oceanodroma homochroa	0.14 ± 0.04	0.24 ± 0.06	0.09 ± 0.02
Black	Oceanodroma melania	0.01 ± 0.01	0.08 ± 0.02	0.02 ± 0.01
Leach's	Oceanodroma leucorhoa	0.03 ± 0.01	0.15 ± 0.03	0.16 ± 0.03
Tropicbirds	Phaethontidae	0.00 ± 0.00	0.00 ± 0.00	0.00 ± 0.00
Red-billed	Phaethon aethereus	0.00 ± 0.00	0.00 ± 0.00	0.00 ± 0.00
Pelicans	Pelecanidae	0.00 ± 0.00	0.00 ± 0.00	0.01 ± 0.01
Brown	Pelecanus occidentalis	0.00 ± 0.00	0.00 ± 0.00	0.01 ± 0.01
Cormorants	Phalacrocoracidae	0.08 ± 0.03	0.21 ± 0.07	0.20 ± 0.10
Brandt's	Phalacrocorax penicillatus	0.05 ± 0.02	0.19 ± 0.07	0.16 ± 0.10
Double-crested	Phalacrocorax auritus	0.01 ± 0.01	0.01 ± 0.01	0.01 ± 0.01
Pelagic	Phalacrocorax pelagicus	0.00 ± 0.00	0.00 ± 0.00	0.00 ± 0.00
Sea ducks	Anatidae	0.00 ± 0.00	0.00 ± 0.00	0.00 ± 0.00
Brant	Branta bernicla	0.00 ± 0.00	0.00 ± 0.00	0.00 ± 0.00
Red-breasted Merganser	Mergus serrator	0.00 ± 0.00	0.00 ± 0.00	0.00 ± 0.00
Surf Scoter	Melanitta perspicillata	0.00 ± 0.00	0.00 ± 0.00	0.00 ± 0.00
White-winged Scoter	Melanitta fusca	0.00 ± 0.00	0.00 ± 0.00	0.00 ± 0.00

TABLE 1E. CONTINUED.

Species		S5 (South)		
		September	May	January
Larids	Laridae	1.13 ± 0.19	0.68 ± 0.14	1.87 ± 0.23
Gulls	Larinae	0.76 ± 0.18	0.58 ± 0.13	1.80 ± 0.22
Black-legged Kittiwake	Rissa tridactyla	0.00 ± 0.00	0.00 ± 0.00	0.59 ± 0.08
Bonaparte's	Larus philadelphia	0.00 ± 0.00	0.03 ± 0.01	0.19 ± 0.15
California	Larus californicus	0.01 ± 0.01	0.00 ± 0.00	0.30 ± 0.06
Glaucous	Larus hyperboreus	0.00 ± 0.00	0.00 ± 0.00	0.00 ± 0.00
Glaucous-winged	Larus glaucescens	0.00 ± 0.00	0.00 ± 0.00	0.00 ± 0.00
Heermann's	Larus heermanni	0.04 ± 0.04	0.00 ± 0.00	0.01 ± 0.01
Herring	Larus argentatus	0.00 ± 0.00	0.00 ± 0.00	0.00 ± 0.00
Mew	Larus canus	0.00 ± 0.00	0.00 ± 0.00	0.00 ± 0.00
Ring-billed	Larus delawarensis	0.00 ± 0.00	0.00 ± 0.00	0.00 ± 0.00
Sabine's	Xema sabini	0.05 ± 0.02	0.05 ± 0.02	0.00 ± 0.00
Western	Larus occidentalis	0.64 ± 0.17	0.48 ± 0.13	0.57 ± 0.10
Terns	Sterninae	0.29 ± 0.06	0.07 ± 0.03	0.01 ± 0.01
Caspian	Hydroprogne caspia	0.00 ± 0.00	0.00 ± 0.00	0.00 ± 0.00
Common/Arctic	Sterna hirundo/paradisaea	0.29 ± 0.06	0.07 ± 0.03	0.01 ± 0.01
Elegant	Thalasseus elegans	0.00 ± 0.00	0.00 ± 0.00	0.00 ± 0.00
Elegant/Royal	Thalasseus elegans/maximus	0.00 ± 0.00	0.00 ± 0.00	0.00 ± 0.00
Forster's	Sterna forsteri	0.00 ± 0.00	0.00 ± 0.00	0.00 ± 0.00
Least	Sterna antillarum	0.00 ± 0.00	0.00 ± 0.00	0.00 ± 0.00
Royal	Thalasseus maximus	0.00 ± 0.00	0.00 ± 0.00	0.00 ± 0.00
Jaegers and skuas	Stercorariinae	0.08 ± 0.02	0.02 ± 0.01	0.05 ± 0.02
Long-tailed Jaeger	Stercorarius longicaudus	0.00 ± 0.00	0.00 ± 0.00	0.00 ± 0.00
Parasitic Jaeger	Stercorarius parasiticus	0.00 ± 0.00	0.00 ± 0.00	0.00 ± 0.00
Pomarine Jaeger	Stercorarius pomarinus	0.05 ± 0.02	0.02 ± 0.01	0.02 ± 0.01
South Polar Skua	Stercorarius maccormicki	0.00 ± 0.00	0.00 ± 0.00	0.00 ± 0.00
Alcids	Alcidae	0.03 ± 0.01	0.23 ± 0.05	1.42 ± 0.16
Cassin's Auklet	Ptychoramphus aleuticus	0.00 ± 0.00	0.02 ± 0.01	0.84 ± 0.13
Common Murre	Uria aalge	0.00 ± 0.00	0.00 ± 0.00	0.00 ± 0.00
Pigeon Guillemots	Cepphus columba	0.00 ± 0.00	0.00 ± 0.00	0.43 ± 0.08
Rhinoceros Auklet	Cerorhinca monocerata	0.00 ± 0.00	0.01 ± 0.01	0.00 ± 0.00
Xantus's Murrelet	Synthliboramphus hypoleucus	0.00 ± 0.00	0.18 ± 0.05	0.00 ± 0.00
Phalaropes	Phalaropodinae	0.47 ± 0.08	0.61 ± 0.11	1.13 ± 0.22
Red	Phalaropus fulicarius	0.26 ± 0.06	0.02 ± 0.01	0.66 ± 0.14
Red-necked	Phalaropus lobatus	0.02 ± 0.01	0.17 ± 0.04	0.02 ± 0.01

TABLE 2A. DENSITIES (BIRDS/KM² ± SE) OF SEABIRDS ALONG ALL COASTLINES WITHIN THE STUDY AREA DURING JANUARY, MAY, AND SEPTEMBER FROM 1999–2002.

Species		January	May	September
			All coastlines	
All seabirds		114.2 ± 8.58	39.77 ± 3.51	58.73 ± 15.63
Loons	Gaviidae	5.16 ± 0.71	0.70 ± 0.14	0.03 ± 0.01
Common	Gavia immer	0.15 ± 0.03	0.08 ± 0.01	0.00 ± 0.00
Pacific	Gavia pacifica	1.66 ± 0.17	0.56 ± 0.14	0.00 ± 0.00
Red-throated	Gavia stellata	0.13 ± 0.03	0.00 ± 0.00	0.00 ± 0.00
Grebes	Podicipedidae	35.20 ± 4.48	20.39 ± 3.02	6.36 ± 1.65
Horned	Podiceps auritus	0.00 ± 0.00	0.00 ± 0.00	0.00 ± 0.00
Pied-billed	Podilymbus podiceps	0.00 ± 0.00	0.00 ± 0.00	0.00 ± 0.00
Western	Aechmophorus occidentalis	34.89 ± 4.48	20.38 ± 3.02	6.34 ± 1.65
Albatrosses	Diomedeidae	0.00 ± 0.00	0.00 ± 0.00	0.00 ± 0.00
Black-footed	Phoebastria nigripes	0.00 ± 0.00	0.00 ± 0.00	0.00 ± 0.00
Laysan	Phoebastria immutabilis	0.00 ± 0.00	0.00 ± 0.00	0.00 ± 0.00
Shearwaters and fulmars	Procellariidae	0.02 ± 0.01	0.13 ± 0.07	19.70 ± 14.86
Buller's Shearwater	Puffinus bulleri	0.00 ± 0.00	0.00 ± 0.00	0.00 ± 0.00
Black-vented Shearwater	Puffinus opisthomelas	0.00 ± 0.00	0.00 ± 0.00	0.00 ± 0.00
Northern Fulmar	Fulmarus glacialis	0.00 ± 0.00	0.00 ± 0.00	0.00 ± 0.00
Pink-footed Shearwater	Puffinus creatopus	0.00 ± 0.00	0.00 ± 0.00	0.01 ± 0.01
Sooty Shearwater	Puffinus griseus	0.01 ± 0.01	0.09 ± 0.07	19.56 ± 14.86
Storm-Petrels	Hydrobatidae	0.00 ± 0.00	0.00 ± 0.00	0.00 ± 0.00
Ashy	Oceanodroma homochroa	0.00 ± 0.00	0.00 ± 0.00	0.00 ± 0.00
Black	Oceanodroma melania	0.00 ± 0.00	0.00 ± 0.00	0.00 ± 0.00
Leach's	Oceanodroma leucorhoa	0.00 ± 0.00	0.00 ± 0.00	0.00 ± 0.00
Tropicbirds	Phaethontidae	0.00 ± 0.00	0.00 ± 0.00	0.00 ± 0.00
Red-billed	Phaethon aethereus	0.00 ± 0.00	0.00 ± 0.00	0.00 ± 0.00
Pelicans	Pelecanidae	1.26 ± 0.12	1.77 ± 0.47	3.80 ± 0.78
Brown	Pelecanus occidentalis	1.26 ± 0.12	1.77 ± 0.47	3.80 ± 0.78
Cormorants	Phalacrocoracidae	3.66 ± 0.48	3.90 ± 0.63	3.86 ± 0.73
Brandt's	Phalacrocorax penicillatus	1.62 ± 0.17	1.61 ± 0.16	1.31 ± 0.20
Double-crested	Phalacrocorax auritus	0.46 ± 0.07	0.31 ± 0.04	0.41 ± 0.05
Pelagic	Phalacrocorax pelagicus	0.16 ± 0.02	0.10 ± 0.02	0.00 ± 0.00
Sea ducks	Anatidae	11.25 ± 1.92	2.36 ± 0.74	0.10 ± 0.05
Brant	Branta bernicla	0.02 ± 0.02	0.05 ± 0.04	0.00 ± 0.00
Red-breasted Merganser	Mergus serrator	0.05 ± 0.02	0.00 ± 0.00	0.00 ± 0.00
Surf Scoter	Melanitta perspicillata	11.09 ± 1.91	2.31 ± 0.74	0.10 ± 0.05
White-winged Scoter	Melanitta fusca	0.01 ± 0.01	0.00 ± 0.00	0.00 ± 0.00

TABLE 2A. CONTINUED.

Species		All coastlines		
		January	May	September
Larids	Laridae	57.06 ± 6.86	10.11 ± 0.86	24.67 ± 3.78
Gulls	Larinae	56.22 ± 6.85	8.99 ± 0.85	21.61 ± 3.69
Black-legged Kittiwake	*Rissa tridactyla*	0.03 ± 0.01	0.00 ± 0.00	0.00 ± 0.00
Bonaparte's	*Larus philadelphia*	0.21 ± 0.12	0.16 ± 0.15	0.00 ± 0.00
California	*Larus californicus*	37.45 ± 5.92	0.30 ± 0.06	0.81 ± 0.23
Glaucous	*Larus hyperboreus*	0.00 ± 0.00	0.00 ± 0.00	0.00 ± 0.00
Glaucous-winged	*Larus glaucescens*	0.05 ± 0.01	0.00 ± 0.00	0.01 ± 0.01
Heermann's	*Larus heermanni*	1.75 ± 0.39	0.05 ± 0.01	3.59 ± 0.64
Herring	*Larus argentatus*	0.02 ± 0.01	0.00 ± 0.00	0.00 ± 0.00
Mew	*Larus canus*	0.04 ± 0.02	0.00 ± 0.00	0.00 ± 0.00
Ring-billed	*Larus delawarensis*	0.15 ± 0.05	0.00 ± 0.00	0.00 ± 0.00
Sabine's	*Xema sabini*	0.00 ± 0.00	0.00 ± 0.00	0.00 ± 0.00
Western	*Larus occidentalis*	14.43 ± 3.12	8.04 ± 0.80	16.25 ± 3.46
Terns	Sterninae	0.84 ± 0.35	1.11 ± 0.16	3.04 ± 0.54
Caspian	*Hydroprogne caspia*	0.03 ± 0.01	0.19 ± 0.03	0.48 ± 0.09
Common/Arctic	*Sterna hirundo/paradisaea*	0.00 ± 0.00	0.00 ± 0.00	0.00 ± 0.00
Elegant	*Thalasseus elegans*	0.01 ± 0.01	0.23 ± 0.05	0.54 ± 0.12
Elegant/Royal	*Thalasseus elegans/maximus*	0.61 ± 0.34	0.26 ± 0.06	1.88 ± 0.46
Forster's	*Sterna forsteri*	0.10 ± 0.03	0.17 ± 0.04	0.06 ± 0.02
Least	*Sterna antillarum*	0.00 ± 0.00	0.16 ± 0.07	0.00 ± 0.00
Royal	*Thalasseus maximus*	0.07 ± 0.02	0.00 ± 0.00	0.04 ± 0.02
Jaegers and skuas	Stercorariinae	0.00 ± 0.00	0.00 ± 0.00	0.01 ± 0.01
Long-tailed Jaeger	*Stercorarius longicaudus*	0.00 ± 0.00	0.00 ± 0.00	0.00 ± 0.00
Parasitic Jaeger	*Stercorarius parasiticus*	0.00 ± 0.00	0.00 ± 0.00	0.01 ± 0.00
Pomarine Jaeger	*Stercorarius pomarinus*	0.00 ± 0.00	0.00 ± 0.00	0.00 ± 0.00
South Polar Skua	*Stercorarius maccormicki*	0.00 ± 0.00	0.00 ± 0.00	0.00 ± 0.00
Alcids	Alcidae	0.14 ± 0.05	0.27 ± 0.06	0.03 ± 0.01
Cassin's Auklet	*Ptychoramphus aleuticus*	0.08 ± 0.04	0.01 ± 0.01	0.03 ± 0.01
Common Murre	*Uria aalge*	0.02 ± 0.01	0.00 ± 0.00	0.00 ± 0.00
Pigeon Guillemots	*Cepphus columba*	0.00 ± 0.00	0.26 ± 0.06	0.00 ± 0.00
Rhinoceros Auklet	*Cerorhinca monocerata*	0.02 ± 0.01	0.00 ± 0.00	0.02 ± 0.01
Xantus's Murrelet	*Synthliboramphus hypoleucus*	0.00 ± 0.00	0.00 ± 0.00	0.00 ± 0.00
Phalaropes	Phalaropodinae	0.02 ± 0.01	0.04 ± 0.03	0.06 ± 0.02
Red	*Phalaropus fulicarius*	0.00 ± 0.00	0.00 ± 0.00	0.00 ± 0.00
Red-necked	*Phalaropus lobatus*	0.00 ± 0.00	0.00 ± 0.00	0.01 ± 0.01

TABLE 2B. DENSITIES (BIRDS/KM^2 ± SE) OF SEABIRDS ALONG MAINLAND COASTLINES WITHIN THE STUDY AREA DURING JANUARY, MAY, AND SEPTEMBER FROM 1999-2002.

Species		Mainland coastline		
		January	May	September
All seabirds		141.6 ± 13.99	56.23 ± 6.08	95.41 ± 31.71
Loons	Gaviidae	7.27 ± 1.26	0.84 ± 0.23	0.06 ± 0.02
Common	Gavia immer	0.16 ± 0.04	0.10 ± 0.02	0.00 ± 0.00
Pacific	Gavia pacifica	1.58 ± 0.22	0.67 ± 0.23	0.00 ± 0.00
Red-throated	Gavia stellata	0.23 ± 0.05	0.00 ± 0.00	0.00 ± 0.00
Grebes	Podicipedidae	65.94 ± 7.96	37.42 ± 5.34	12.97 ± 3.33
Horned	Podiceps auritus	0.01 ± 0.01	0.00 ± 0.00	0.00 ± 0.00
Pied-billed	Podilymbus podiceps	0.00 ± 0.00	0.00 ± 0.00	0.00 ± 0.00
Western	Aechmophorus occidentalis	65.70 ± 7.96	37.40 ± 5.34	12.94 ± 3.33
Albatrosses	Diomedeidae	0.00 ± 0.00	0.00 ± 0.00	0.00 ± 0.00
Black-footed	Phoebastria nigripes	0.00 ± 0.00	0.00 ± 0.00	0.00 ± 0.00
Laysan	Phoebastria immutabilis	0.00 ± 0.00	0.00 ± 0.00	0.00 ± 0.00
Shearwaters and fulmars	Procellariidae	0.00 ± 0.00	0.00 ± 0.00	39.87 ± 30.40
Buller's Shearwater	Puffinus bulleri	0.00 ± 0.00	0.00 ± 0.00	0.00 ± 0.00
Black-vented Shearwater	Puffinus opisthomelas	0.00 ± 0.00	0.00 ± 0.00	0.00 ± 0.00
Northern Fulmar	Fulmarus glacialis	0.00 ± 0.00	0.00 ± 0.00	0.00 ± 0.00
Pink-footed Shearwater	Puffinus creatopus	0.00 ± 0.00	0.00 ± 0.00	0.00 ± 0.00
Sooty Shearwater	Puffinus griseus	0.00 ± 0.00	0.00 ± 0.00	39.86 ± 30.40
Storm-Petrels	Hydrobatidae	0.00 ± 0.00	0.00 ± 0.00	0.00 ± 0.00
Ashy	Oceanodroma homochroa	0.00 ± 0.00	0.00 ± 0.00	0.00 ± 0.00
Black	Oceanodroma melania	0.00 ± 0.00	0.00 ± 0.00	0.00 ± 0.00
Leach's	Oceanodroma leucorhoa	0.00 ± 0.00	0.00 ± 0.00	0.00 ± 0.00
Tropicbirds	Phaethontidae	0.00 ± 0.00	0.00 ± 0.00	0.00 ± 0.00
Red-billed	Phaethon aethereus	0.00 ± 0.00	0.00 ± 0.00	0.00 ± 0.00
Pelicans	Pelecanidae	1.49 ± 0.20	2.58 ± 0.86	4.51 ± 0.85
Brown	Pelecanus occidentalis	1.49 ± 0.20	2.58 ± 0.86	4.51 ± 0.85
Cormorants	Phalacrocoracidae	2.54 ± 0.27	3.68 ± 0.97	2.60 ± 0.45
Brandt's	Phalacrocorax penicillatus	1.04 ± 0.17	0.89 ± 0.18	0.61 ± 0.09
Double-crested	Phalacrocorax auritus	0.73 ± 0.12	0.39 ± 0.06	0.70 ± 0.10
Pelagic	Phalacrocorax pelagicus	0.07 ± 0.02	0.05 ± 0.02	0.00 ± 0.00
Sea ducks	Anatidae	12.48 ± 3.30	3.85 ± 1.32	0.20 ± 0.10
Brant	Branta bernicla	0.04 ± 0.04	0.09 ± 0.07	0.00 ± 0.00
Red-breasted Merganser	Mergus serrator	0.09 ± 0.03	0.00 ± 0.00	0.00 ± 0.00
Surf Scoter	Melanitta perspicillata	12.18 ± 3.28	3.75 ± 1.32	0.20 ± 0.10
White-winged Scoter	Melanitta fusca	0.02 ± 0.02	0.00 ± 0.00	0.00 ± 0.00

TABLE 2B. CONTINUED.

Species		Mainland coastline		
		January	May	September
Larids	Laridae	51.40 ± 10.47	7.56 ± 0.83	34.98 ± 7.51
Gulls	Larinae	50.84 ± 10.46	5.53 ± 0.76	29.85 ± 7.34
Black-legged Kittiwake	*Rissa tridactyla*	0.00 ± 0.00	0.00 ± 0.00	0.00 ± 0.00
Bonaparte's	*Larus philadelphia*	0.39 ± 0.23	0.30 ± 0.28	0.00 ± 0.00
California	*Larus californicus*	31.45 ± 8.62	0.36 ± 0.10	1.52 ± 0.46
Glaucous	*Larus hyperboreus*	0.00 ± 0.00	0.00 ± 0.00	0.00 ± 0.00
Glaucous-winged	*Larus glaucescens*	0.07 ± 0.02	0.00 ± 0.00	0.02 ± 0.02
Heermann's	*Larus heermanni*	1.09 ± 0.17	0.07 ± 0.02	5.65 ± 1.25
Herring	*Larus argentatus*	0.02 ± 0.01	0.00 ± 0.00	0.01 ± 0.01
Mew	*Larus canus*	0.06 ± 0.04	0.00 ± 0.00	0.00 ± 0.00
Ring-billed	*Larus delawarensis*	0.27 ± 0.09	0.00 ± 0.00	0.00 ± 0.00
Sabine's	*Xema sabini*	0.00 ± 0.00	0.00 ± 0.00	0.00 ± 0.00
Western	*Larus occidentalis*	14.41 ± 5.43	4.15 ± 0.57	20.98 ± 6.91
Terns	Sterninae	0.56 ± 0.09	2.03 ± 0.28	5.11 ± 1.00
Caspian	*Hydroprogne caspia*	0.05 ± 0.02	0.34 ± 0.06	0.90 ± 0.17
Common/Arctic	*Sterna hirundo/paradisaea*	0.00 ± 0.00	0.00 ± 0.00	0.00 ± 0.00
Elegant	*Thalasseus elegans*	0.01 ± 0.01	0.42 ± 0.09	1.09 ± 0.23
Elegant/Royal	*Thalasseus elegans/maximus*	0.27 ± 0.06	0.48 ± 0.10	2.90 ± 0.82
Forster's	*Sterna forsteri*	0.18 ± 0.06	0.31 ± 0.07	0.12 ± 0.04
Least	*Sterna antillarum*	0.00 ± 0.00	0.30 ± 0.12	0.01 ± 0.01
Royal	*Thalasseus maximus*	0.02 ± 0.01	0.00 ± 0.00	0.01 ± 0.01
Jaegers and skuas	Stercorariinae	0.00 ± 0.00	0.00 ± 0.00	0.02 ± 0.01
Long-tailed Jaeger	*Stercorarius longicaudus*	0.00 ± 0.00	0.00 ± 0.00	0.00 ± 0.00
Parasitic Jaeger	*Stercorarius parasiticus*	0.00 ± 0.00	0.00 ± 0.00	0.02 ± 0.01
Pomarine Jaeger	*Stercorarius pomarinus*	0.00 ± 0.00	0.00 ± 0.00	0.00 ± 0.00
South Polar Skua	*Stercorarius maccormicki*	0.00 ± 0.00	0.00 ± 0.00	0.00 ± 0.00
Alcids	Alcidae	0.05 ± 0.02	0.15 ± 0.09	0.00 ± 0.00
Cassin's Auklet	*Ptychoramphus aleuticus*	0.00 ± 0.00	0.00 ± 0.00	0.00 ± 0.00
Common Murre	*Uria aalge*	0.04 ± 0.02	0.00 ± 0.00	0.00 ± 0.00
Pigeon Guillemots	*Cepphus columba*	0.00 ± 0.00	0.15 ± 0.09	0.00 ± 0.00
Rhinoceros Auklet	*Cerorhinca monocerata*	0.00 ± 0.00	0.00 ± 0.00	0.00 ± 0.00
Xantus's Murrelet	*Synthliboramphus hypoleucus*	0.00 ± 0.00	0.00 ± 0.00	0.00 ± 0.00
Phalaropes	Phalaropodinae	0.03 ± 0.02	0.00 ± 0.00	0.05 ± 0.04
Red	*Phalaropus fulicarius*	0.00 ± 0.00	0.00 ± 0.00	0.00 ± 0.00
Red-necked	*Phalaropus lobatus*	0.00 ± 0.00	0.00 ± 0.00	0.00 ± 0.00

TABLE 2C. DENSITIES (BIRDS/KM^2 ± SE) OF SEABIRDS ALONG ISLAND COASTLINES WITHIN THE STUDY AREA DURING JANUARY, MAY, AND SEPTEMBER FROM 1999–2002.

Species		Island coastlines		
		January	May	September
All seabirds		83.32 ± 8.69	20.18 ± 1.90	23.58 ± 3.26
Loons	Gaviidae	2.79 ± 0.45	0.53 ± 0.15	0.00 ± 0.00
Common	Gavia immer	0.14 ± 0.04	0.04 ± 0.02	0.00 ± 0.00
Pacific	Gavia pacifica	1.74 ± 0.27	0.43 ± 0.14	0.00 ± 0.00
Red-throated	Gavia stellata	0.01 ± 0.01	0.00 ± 0.00	0.00 ± 0.00
Grebes	Podicipedidae	0.56 ± 0.36	0.12 ± 0.06	0.02 ± 0.02
Horned	Podiceps auritus	0.00 ± 0.00	0.00 ± 0.00	0.00 ± 0.00
Pied-billed	Podilymbus podiceps	0.00 ± 0.00	0.00 ± 0.00	0.00 ± 0.00
Western	Aechmophorus occidentalis	0.17 ± 0.08	0.12 ± 0.06	0.02 ± 0.02
Albatrosses	Diomedeidae	0.00 ± 0.00	0.00 ± 0.00	0.00 ± 0.00
Black-footed	Phoebastria nigripes	0.00 ± 0.00	0.00 ± 0.00	0.00 ± 0.00
Laysan	Phoebastria immutabilis	0.00 ± 0.00	0.00 ± 0.00	0.00 ± 0.00
Shearwaters and fulmars	Procellariidae	0.03 ± 0.03	0.29 ± 0.16	0.37 ± 0.32
Buller's Shearwater	Puffinus bulleri	0.00 ± 0.00	0.00 ± 0.00	0.00 ± 0.00
Black-vented Shearwater	Puffinus opisthomelas	0.00 ± 0.00	0.00 ± 0.00	0.01 ± 0.01
Northern Fulmar	Fulmarus glacialis	0.00 ± 0.00	0.01 ± 0.01	0.00 ± 0.00
Pink-footed Shearwater	Puffinus creatopus	0.00 ± 0.00	0.00 ± 0.00	0.02 ± 0.01
Sooty Shearwater	Puffinus griseus	0.03 ± 0.03	0.19 ± 0.14	0.10 ± 0.07
Storm-Petrels	Hydrobatidae	0.00 ± 0.00	0.00 ± 0.00	0.00 ± 0.00
Ashy	Oceanodroma homochroa	0.00 ± 0.00	0.00 ± 0.00	0.00 ± 0.00
Black	Oceanodroma melania	0.00 ± 0.00	0.00 ± 0.00	0.00 ± 0.00
Leach's	Oceanodroma leucorhoa	0.00 ± 0.00	0.00 ± 0.00	0.00 ± 0.00
Tropicbirds	Phaethontidae	0.00 ± 0.00	0.00 ± 0.00	0.00 ± 0.00
Red-billed	Phaethon aethereus	0.00 ± 0.00	0.00 ± 0.00	0.00 ± 0.00
Pelicans	Pelecanidae	1.00 ± 0.14	0.81 ± 0.11	3.12 ± 1.30
Brown	Pelecanus occidentalis	1.00 ± 0.14	0.81 ± 0.11	3.12 ± 1.30
Cormorants	Phalacrocoracidae	4.92 ± 0.97	4.17 ± 0.77	5.08 ± 1.36
Brandt's	Phalacrocorax penicillatus	2.28 ± 0.31	2.46 ± 0.26	1.98 ± 0.38
Double-crested	Phalacrocorax auritus	0.15 ± 0.03	0.22 ± 0.05	0.14 ± 0.03
Pelagic	Phalacrocorax pelagicus	0.27 ± 0.05	0.16 ± 0.03	0.00 ± 0.00
Sea Ducks	Anatidae	9.87 ± 1.68	0.59 ± 0.33	0.00 ± 0.00
Brant	Branta bernicla	0.00 ± 0.00	0.00 ± 0.00	0.00 ± 0.00
Red-breasted Merganser	Mergus serrator	0.00 ± 0.00	0.00 ± 0.00	0.00 ± 0.00
Surf Scoter	Melanitta perspicillata	9.87 ± 1.68	0.59 ± 0.33	0.00 ± 0.00
White-winged Scoter	Melanitta fusca	0.00 ± 0.00	0.00 ± 0.00	0.00 ± 0.00

TABLE 2C. CONTINUED.

Species		Island coastlines		
		January	May	September
Larids	Laridae	63.45 ± 8.61	13.13 ± 1.58	14.78 ± 1.48
Gulls	Larinae	62.30 ± 8.59	13.11 ± 1.58	13.72 ± 1.44
Black-legged Kittiwake	*Rissa tridactyla*	0.07 ± 0.03	0.00 ± 0.00	0.00 ± 0.00
Bonaparte's	*Larus philadelphia*	0.00 ± 0.00	0.00 ± 0.00	0.00 ± 0.00
California	*Larus californicus*	44.21 ± 8.03	0.23 ± 0.07	0.13 ± 0.03
Glaucous	*Larus hyperboreus*	0.00 ± 0.00	0.00 ± 0.00	0.00 ± 0.00
Glaucous-winged	*Larus glaucescens*	0.03 ± 0.02	0.00 ± 0.00	0.00 ± 0.00
Heermann's	*Larus heermanni*	2.49 ± 0.81	0.01 ± 0.01	1.61 ± 0.30
Herring	*Larus argentatus*	0.02 ± 0.01	0.00 ± 0.00	0.00 ± 0.00
Mew	*Larus canus*	0.00 ± 0.00	0.00 ± 0.00	0.00 ± 0.00
Ring-billed	*Larus delawarensis*	0.00 ± 0.00	0.00 ± 0.00	0.00 ± 0.00
Sabine's	*Xema sabini*	0.00 ± 0.00	0.00 ± 0.00	0.00 ± 0.00
Western	*Larus occidentalis*	14.46 ± 2.57	12.67 ± 1.54	11.73 ± 1.38
Terns	Sterninae	1.15 ± 0.73	0.01 ± 0.01	1.05 ± 0.43
Caspian	*Hydroprogne caspia*	0.01 ± 0.01	0.01 ± 0.01	0.07 ± 0.03
Common/Arctic	*Sterna hirundo/paradisaea*	0.00 ± 0.00	0.00 ± 0.00	0.00 ± 0.00
Elegant	*Thalasseus elegans*	0.00 ± 0.00	0.00 ± 0.00	0.00 ± 0.00
Elegant/Royal	*Thalasseus elegans/maximus*	0.99 ± 0.73	0.00 ± 0.00	0.90 ± 0.43
Forster's	*Sterna forsteri*	0.00 ± 0.00	0.00 ± 0.00	0.00 ± 0.00
Least	*Sterna antillarum*	0.00 ± 0.00	0.00 ± 0.00	0.00 ± 0.00
Royal	*Thalasseus maximus*	0.13 ± 0.03	0.00 ± 0.00	0.08 ± 0.03
Jaegers and skuas	Stercorariinae	0.00 ± 0.00	0.00 ± 0.00	0.01 ± 0.01
Long-tailed Jaeger	*Stercorarius longicaudus*	0.00 ± 0.00	0.00 ± 0.00	0.00 ± 0.00
Parasitic Jaeger	*Stercorarius parasiticus*	0.00 ± 0.00	0.00 ± 0.00	0.00 ± 0.00
Pomarine Jaeger	*Stercorarius pomarinus*	0.00 ± 0.00	0.00 ± 0.00	0.00 ± 0.00
South Polar Skua	*Stercorarius maccormicki*	0.00 ± 0.00	0.00 ± 0.00	0.00 ± 0.00
Alcids	Alcidae	0.24 ± 0.10	0.42 ± 0.07	0.05 ± 0.02
Cassin's Auklet	*Ptychoramphus aleuticus*	0.16 ± 0.09	0.02 ± 0.02	0.00 ± 0.00
Common Murre	*Uria aalge*	0.00 ± 0.00	0.00 ± 0.00	0.00 ± 0.00
Pigeon Guillemots	*Cepphus columba*	0.01 ± 0.01	0.39 ± 0.07	0.04 ± 0.02
Rhinoceros Auklet	*Cerorhinca monocerata*	0.04 ± 0.03	0.00 ± 0.00	0.00 ± 0.00
Xantus's Murrelet	*Synthliboramphus hypoleucus*	0.00 ± 0.00	0.00 ± 0.00	0.00 ± 0.00
Phalaropes	Phalaropodinae	0.00 ± 0.00	0.08 ± 0.07	0.07 ± 0.03
Red	*Phalaropus fulicarius*	0.00 ± 0.00	0.00 ± 0.00	0.00 ± 0.00
Red-necked	*Phalaropus lobatus*	0.00 ± 0.00	0.00 ± 0.00	0.01 ± 0.01

TABLE 3A. DENSITIES (BIRDS/KM² ± SE) OF SEABIRDS ALONG THE NORTHERN MAINLAND COASTLINE DURING JANUARY, MAY, AND SEPTEMBER FROM 1999–2002.

Species		Northern mainland coastline		
		January	May	September
All seabirds		72.12 ± 11.15	43.74 ± 12.48	253.8 ± 156.7
Loons	Gaviidae	7.05 ± 1.40	1.98 ± 1.14	0.05 ± 0.03
Common	Gavia immer	0.34 ± 0.14	0.11 ± 0.05	0.00 ± 0.00
Pacific	Gavia pacifica	2.83 ± 0.58	1.69 ± 1.14	0.00 ± 0.00
Red-throated	Gavia stellata	0.16 ± 0.08	0.00 ± 0.00	0.00 ± 0.00
Grebes	Podicipedidae	17.95 ± 4.82	18.88 ± 10.18	12.84 ± 5.06
Horned	Podiceps auritus	0.00 ± 0.00	0.00 ± 0.00	0.00 ± 0.00
Pied-billed	Podilymbus podiceps	0.00 ± 0.00	0.00 ± 0.00	0.00 ± 0.00
Western	Aechmophorus occidentalis	17.47 ± 4.82	18.88 ± 10.18	12.72 ± 5.07
Albatrosses	Diomedeidae	0.00 ± 0.00	0.00 ± 0.00	0.00 ± 0.00
Black-footed	Phoebastria nigripes	0.00 ± 0.00	0.00 ± 0.00	0.00 ± 0.00
Laysan	Phoebastria immutabilis	0.00 ± 0.00	0.00 ± 0.00	0.00 ± 0.00
Shearwaters and fulmars	Procellariidae	0.00 ± 0.00	0.00 ± 0.00	201.5 ± 155.4
Buller's Shearwater	Puffinus bulleri	0.00 ± 0.00	0.00 ± 0.00	0.00 ± 0.00
Black-vented Shearwater	Puffinus opisthomelas	0.00 ± 0.00	0.00 ± 0.00	0.00 ± 0.00
Northern Fulmar	Fulmarus glacialis	0.00 ± 0.00	0.00 ± 0.00	0.00 ± 0.00
Pink-footed Shearwater	Puffinus creatopus	0.00 ± 0.00	0.00 ± 0.00	0.02 ± 0.02
Sooty Shearwater	Puffinus griseus	0.00 ± 0.00	0.00 ± 0.00	201.4 ± 155.4
Storm-Petrels	Hydrobatidae	0.00 ± 0.00	0.00 ± 0.00	0.00 ± 0.00
Ashy	Oceanodroma homochroa	0.00 ± 0.00	0.00 ± 0.00	0.00 ± 0.00
Black	Oceanodroma melania	0.00 ± 0.00	0.00 ± 0.00	0.00 ± 0.00
Leach's	Oceanodroma leucorhoa	0.00 ± 0.00	0.00 ± 0.00	0.00 ± 0.00
Tropicbirds	Phaethontidae	0.00 ± 0.00	0.00 ± 0.00	0.00 ± 0.00
Red-billed	Phaethon aethereus	0.00 ± 0.00	0.00 ± 0.00	0.00 ± 0.00
Pelicans	Pelecanidae	1.36 ± 0.38	1.23 ± 0.45	5.09 ± 2.62
Brown	Pelecanus occidentalis	1.36 ± 0.38	1.23 ± 0.45	5.09 ± 2.62
Cormorants	Phalacrocoracidae	2.20 ± 0.51	3.31 ± 0.69	4.15 ± 0.51
Brandt's	Phalacrocorax penicillatus	1.36 ± 0.41	1.55 ± 0.46	1.68 ± 0.34
Double-crested	Phalacrocorax auritus	0.27 ± 0.09	0.43 ± 0.16	0.57 ± 0.18
Pelagic	Phalacrocorax pelagicus	0.18 ± 0.07	0.25 ± 0.08	0.02 ± 0.02
Sea ducks	Anatidae	20.49 ± 7.43	12.98 ± 6.87	0.67 ± 0.45
Brant	Branta bernicla	0.00 ± 0.00	0.27 ± 0.27	0.67 ± 0.45
Red-breasted Merganser	Mergus serrator	0.02 ± 0.02	0.00 ± 0.00	0.00 ± 0.00
Surf Scoter	Melanitta perspicillata	19.61 ± 7.14	12.70 ± 6.87	0.67 ± 0.45
White-winged Scoter	Melanitta fusca	0.09 ± 0.09	0.00 ± 0.00	0.00 ± 0.00

TABLE 3A. CONTINUED.

Species		Northern mainland coastline		
		January	May	September
Larids	Laridae	22.42 ± 4.88	4.29 ± 0.76	29.14 ± 10.09
Gulls	Larinae	22.17 ± 4.89	4.20 ± 0.75	28.06 ± 9.95
Black-legged Kittiwake	*Rissa tridactyla*	0.00 ± 0.00	0.00 ± 0.00	0.00 ± 0.00
Bonaparte's	*Larus philadelphia*	0.00 ± 0.00	0.00 ± 0.00	0.00 ± 0.00
California	*Larus californicus*	13.60 ± 4.77	0.39 ± 0.20	3.51 ± 1.44
Glaucous	*Larus hyperboreus*	0.00 ± 0.00	0.00 ± 0.00	0.00 ± 0.00
Glaucous-winged	*Larus glaucescens*	0.11 ± 0.05	0.00 ± 0.00	0.00 ± 0.00
Heermann's	*Larus heermanni*	0.50 ± 0.29	0.02 ± 0.02	11.34 ± 5.44
Herring	*Larus argentatus*	0.05 ± 0.03	0.00 ± 0.00	0.02 ± 0.02
Mew	*Larus canus*	0.05 ± 0.03	0.00 ± 0.00	0.00 ± 0.00
Ring-billed	*Larus delawarensis*	0.23 ± 0.15	0.00 ± 0.00	0.00 ± 0.00
Sabine's	*Xema sabini*	0.00 ± 0.00	0.00 ± 0.00	0.00 ± 0.00
Western	*Larus occidentalis*	5.80 ± 0.89	3.49 ± 0.68	11.39 ± 3.21
Terns	Sterninae	0.25 ± 0.13	0.09 ± 0.06	1.09 ± 0.34
Caspian	*Hydroprogne caspia*	0.00 ± 0.00	0.00 ± 0.00	0.22 ± 0.09
Common/Arctic	*Sterna hirundo/paradisaea*	0.00 ± 0.00	0.00 ± 0.00	0.00 ± 0.00
Elegant	*Thalasseus elegans*	0.00 ± 0.00	0.05 ± 0.05	0.10 ± 0.05
Elegant/Royal	*Thalasseus elegans/maximus*	0.07 ± 0.04	0.00 ± 0.00	0.62 ± 0.25
Forster's	*Sterna forsteri*	0.14 ± 0.10	0.00 ± 0.00	0.02 ± 0.02
Least	*Sterna antillarum*	0.00 ± 0.00	0.05 ± 0.05	0.05 ± 0.05
Royal	*Thalasseus maximus*	0.00 ± 0.00	0.00 ± 0.00	0.00 ± 0.00
Jaegers and skuas	Stercorariinae	0.00 ± 0.00	0.00 ± 0.00	0.00 ± 0.00
Long-tailed Jaeger	*Stercorarius longicaudus*	0.00 ± 0.00	0.00 ± 0.00	0.00 ± 0.00
Parasitic Jaegar	*Stercorarius parasiticus*	0.00 ± 0.00	0.00 ± 0.00	0.00 ± 0.00
Pomarine Jaeger	*Stercorarius pomarinus*	0.00 ± 0.00	0.00 ± 0.00	0.00 ± 0.00
South Polar Skua	*Stercorarius maccormicki*	0.00 ± 0.00	0.00 ± 0.00	0.00 ± 0.00
Alcids	Alcidae	0.16 ± 0.08	0.84 ± 0.46	0.00 ± 0.00
Cassin's Auklet	*Ptychoramphus aleuticus*	0.00 ± 0.00	0.00 ± 0.00	0.00 ± 0.00
Common Murre	*Uria aalge*	0.11 ± 0.07	0.00 ± 0.00	0.00 ± 0.00
Pigeon Guillemots	*Cepphus columba*	0.00 ± 0.00	0.84 ± 0.46	0.00 ± 0.00
Rhinoceros Auklet	*Cerorhinca monocerata*	0.00 ± 0.00	0.00 ± 0.00	0.00 ± 0.00
Xantus's Murrelet	*Synthliboramphus hypoleucus*	0.00 ± 0.00	0.00 ± 0.00	0.00 ± 0.00
Phalaropes	Phalaropodinae	0.11 ± 0.11	0.02 ± 0.02	0.00 ± 0.00
Red	*Phalaropus fulicarius*	0.00 ± 0.00	0.00 ± 0.00	0.00 ± 0.00
Red-necked	*Phalaropus lobatus*	0.00 ± 0.00	0.00 ± 0.00	0.00 ± 0.00

TABLE 3B. DENSITIES (BIRDS/KM^2 ± SE) OF SEABIRDS ALONG THE CENTRAL MAINLAND COASTLINE DURING JANUARY, MAY, AND SEPTEMBER FROM 1999–2002.

Species		Central mainland coastline		
		January	May	September
All seabirds		158.7 ± 22.24	59.62 ± 9.56	66.26 ± 16.79
Loons	Gaviidae	5.31 ± 1.40	0.71 ± 0.16	0.08 ± 0.04
Common	Gavia immer	0.14 ± 0.04	0.12 ± 0.03	0.01 ± 0.01
Pacific	Gavia pacifica	1.65 ± 0.33	0.55 ± 0.14	0.00 ± 0.00
Red-throated	Gavia stellata	0.28 ± 0.07	0.00 ± 0.00	0.00 ± 0.00
Grebes	Podicipedidae	69.12 ± 10.84	39.40 ± 7.93	18.75 ± 6.75
Horned	Podiceps auritus	0.02 ± 0.01	0.00 ± 0.00	0.00 ± 0.00
Pied-billed	Podilymbus podiceps	0.00 ± 0.00	0.01 ± 0.01	0.00 ± 0.00
Western	Aechmophorus occidentalis	68.82 ± 10.84	39.37 ± 7.93	18.74 ± 6.75
Albatrosses	Diomedeidae	0.00 ± 0.00	0.00 ± 0.00	0.00 ± 0.00
Black-footed	Phoebastria nigripes	0.00 ± 0.00	0.00 ± 0.00	0.00 ± 0.00
Laysan	Phoebastria immutabilis	0.00 ± 0.00	0.00 ± 0.00	0.00 ± 0.00
Shearwaters and fulmars	Procellariidae	0.01 ± 0.01	0.01 ± 0.01	0.00 ± 0.00
Buller's Shearwater	Puffinus bulleri	0.00 ± 0.00	0.00 ± 0.00	0.00 ± 0.00
Black-vented Shearwater	Puffinus opisthomelas	0.00 ± 0.00	0.00 ± 0.00	0.00 ± 0.00
Northern Fulmar	Fulmarus glacialis	0.01 ± 0.01	0.00 ± 0.00	0.00 ± 0.00
Pink-footed Shearwater	Puffinus creatopus	0.00 ± 0.00	0.00 ± 0.00	0.00 ± 0.00
Sooty Shearwater	Puffinus griseus	0.00 ± 0.00	0.01 ± 0.01	0.00 ± 0.00
Storm-Petrels	Hydrobatidae	0.00 ± 0.00	0.00 ± 0.00	0.00 ± 0.00
Ashy	Oceanodroma homochroa	0.00 ± 0.00	0.00 ± 0.00	0.00 ± 0.00
Black	Oceanodroma melania	0.00 ± 0.00	0.00 ± 0.00	0.00 ± 0.00
Leach's	Oceanodroma leucorhoa	0.00 ± 0.00	0.00 ± 0.00	0.00 ± 0.00
Tropicbirds	Phaethontidae	0.00 ± 0.00	0.00 ± 0.00	0.00 ± 0.00
Red-billed	Phaethon aethereus	0.00 ± 0.00	0.00 ± 0.00	0.00 ± 0.00
Pelicans	Pelecanidae	1.40 ± 0.24	4.04 ± 1.80	3.73 ± 0.66
Brown	Pelecanus occidentalis	1.40 ± 0.24	4.04 ± 1.80	3.73 ± 0.66
Cormorants	Phalacrocoracidae	3.78 ± 0.47	4.96 ± 1.91	1.97 ± 0.32
Brandt's	Phalacrocorax penicillatus	1.41 ± 0.29	1.01 ± 0.30	0.35 ± 0.09
Double-crested	Phalacrocorax auritus	1.24 ± 0.23	0.49 ± 0.10	1.08 ± 0.18
Pelagic	Phalacrocorax pelagicus	0.06 ± 0.02	0.01 ± 0.01	0.00 ± 0.00
Sea ducks	Anatidae	5.33 ± 0.89	2.03 ± 0.54	0.01 ± 0.01
Brant	Branta bernicla	0.00 ± 0.00	0.09 ± 0.09	0.00 ± 0.00
Red-breasted Merganser	Mergus serrator	0.17 ± 0.07	0.00 ± 0.00	0.00 ± 0.00
Surf Scoter	Melanitta perspicillata	5.15 ± 0.89	1.94 ± 0.52	0.01 ± 0.01
White-winged Scoter	Melanitta fusca	0.00 ± 0.00	0.00 ± 0.00	0.00 ± 0.00

Table 3B. Continued.

Species		Central mainland coastline		
		January	May	September
Larids	Laridae	73.03 ± 19.78	8.35 ± 1.55	41.51 ± 15.54
Gulls	Larinae	72.39 ± 19.77	7.05 ± 1.49	36.22 ± 15.23
Black-legged Kittiwake	Rissa tridactyla	0.00 ± 0.00	0.00 ± 0.00	0.00 ± 0.00
Bonaparte's	Larus philadelphia	0.80 ± 0.46	0.62 ± 0.58	0.00 ± 0.00
California	Larus californicus	45.55 ± 15.93	0.46 ± 0.19	1.62 ± 0.78
Glaucous	Larus hyperboreus	0.00 ± 0.00	0.00 ± 0.00	0.00 ± 0.00
Glaucous-winged	Larus glaucescens	0.08 ± 0.03	0.01 ± 0.01	0.03 ± 0.03
Heermann's	Larus heermanni	1.44 ± 0.31	0.04 ± 0.02	4.61 ± 1.18
Herring	Larus argentatus	0.01 ± 0.01	0.00 ± 0.00	0.01 ± 0.01
Mew	Larus canus	0.03 ± 0.02	0.00 ± 0.00	0.00 ± 0.00
Ring-billed	Larus delawarensis	0.13 ± 0.06	0.00 ± 0.00	0.01 ± 0.01
Sabine's	Xena sabini	0.00 ± 0.00	0.00 ± 0.00	0.00 ± 0.00
Western	Larus occidentalis	21.24 ± 10.86	4.93 ± 1.08	28.92 ± 14.85
Terns	Sterninae	0.64 ± 0.15	1.30 ± 0.34	5.27 ± 1.96
Caspian	Hydroprogne caspia	0.06 ± 0.02	0.24 ± 0.06	0.79 ± 0.24
Common/Arctic	Sterna hirundo/paradisaea	0.00 ± 0.00	0.01 ± 0.01	0.00 ± 0.00
Elegant	Thalasseus elegans	0.00 ± 0.00	0.19 ± 0.07	0.72 ± 0.30
Elegant/Royal	Thalasseus elegans/maximus	0.28 ± 0.11	0.11 ± 0.04	3.62 ± 1.70
Forster's	Sterna forsteri	0.25 ± 0.10	0.31 ± 0.10	0.10 ± 0.04
Least	Sterna antillarum	0.00 ± 0.00	0.29 ± 0.25	0.00 ± 0.00
Royal	Thalasseus maximus	0.04 ± 0.02	0.00 ± 0.00	0.00 ± 0.00
Jaegers and skuas	Stercorariinae	0.00 ± 0.00	0.00 ± 0.00	0.02 ± 0.02
Long-tailed Jaeger	Stercorarius longicaudus	0.00 ± 0.00	0.00 ± 0.00	0.00 ± 0.00
Parasitic Jaegar	Stercorarius parasiticus	0.00 ± 0.00	0.00 ± 0.00	0.02 ± 0.02
Pomarine Jaeger	Stercorarius pomarinus	0.00 ± 0.00	0.00 ± 0.00	0.00 ± 0.00
South Polar Skua	Stercorarius maccormicki	0.00 ± 0.00	0.00 ± 0.00	0.00 ± 0.00
Alcids	Alcidae	0.04 ± 0.03	0.00 ± 0.00	0.00 ± 0.00
Cassin's Auklet	Ptychoramphus aleuticus	0.00 ± 0.00	0.00 ± 0.00	0.00 ± 0.00
Common Murre	Uria aalge	0.04 ± 0.03	0.00 ± 0.00	0.00 ± 0.00
Pigeon Guillemots	Cepphus columba	0.00 ± 0.00	0.00 ± 0.00	0.00 ± 0.00
Rhinoceros Auklet	Cerorhinca monocerata	0.00 ± 0.00	0.00 ± 0.00	0.00 ± 0.00
Xantus's Murrelet	Synthliboramphus hypoleucus	0.00 ± 0.00	0.00 ± 0.00	0.00 ± 0.00
Phalaropes	Phalaropodinae	0.02 ± 0.02	0.00 ± 0.00	0.12 ± 0.08
Red	Phalaropus fulicarius	0.00 ± 0.00	0.00 ± 0.00	0.01 ± 0.01
Red-necked	Phalaropus lobatus	0.00 ± 0.00	0.00 ± 0.00	0.00 ± 0.00

TABLE 3C. DENSITIES (BIRDS/KM² ± SE) OF SEABIRDS ALONG THE SOUTHERN MAINLAND COASTLINE DURING JANUARY, MAY, AND SEPTEMBER FROM 1999–2002.

Species		January	Southern mainland coastline May	September
All seabirds		155.0 ± 25.55	58.22 ± 9.81	43.26 ± 6.90
Loons	Gaviidae	10.33 ± 3.13	0.42 ± 0.19	0.04 ± 0.02
Common	Gavia immer	0.08 ± 0.05	0.07 ± 0.03	0.00 ± 0.00
Pacific	Gavia pacifica	0.78 ± 0.34	0.30 ± 0.19	0.01 ± 0.01
Red-throated	Gavia stellata	0.20 ± 0.09	0.01 ± 0.01	0.00 ± 0.00
Grebes	Podicipedidae	88.10 ± 17.47	44.55 ± 9.50	5.42 ± 2.18
Horned	Podiceps auritus	0.00 ± 0.00	0.00 ± 0.00	0.00 ± 0.00
Pied-billed	Podilymbus podiceps	0.00 ± 0.00	0.00 ± 0.00	0.00 ± 0.00
Western	Aechmophorus occidentalis	88.07 ± 17.47	44.55 ± 9.50	5.42 ± 2.18
Albatrosses	Diomedeidae	0.00 ± 0.00	0.00 ± 0.00	0.00 ± 0.00
Black-footed	Phoebastria nigripes	0.00 ± 0.00	0.00 ± 0.00	0.00 ± 0.00
Laysan	Phoebastria immutabilis	0.00 ± 0.00	0.00 ± 0.00	0.00 ± 0.00
Shearwaters and fulmars	Procellariidae	0.00 ± 0.00	0.00 ± 0.00	0.00 ± 0.00
Buller's Shearwater	Puffinus bulleri	0.00 ± 0.00	0.00 ± 0.00	0.00 ± 0.00
Black-vented Shearwater	Puffinus opisthomelas	0.00 ± 0.00	0.00 ± 0.00	0.00 ± 0.00
Northern Fulmar	Fulmarus glacialis	0.00 ± 0.00	0.00 ± 0.00	0.00 ± 0.00
Pink-footed Shearwater	Puffinus creatopus	0.00 ± 0.00	0.00 ± 0.00	0.00 ± 0.00
Sooty Shearwater	Puffinus griseus	0.00 ± 0.00	0.00 ± 0.00	0.00 ± 0.00
Storm-Petrels	Hydrobatidae	0.00 ± 0.00	0.00 ± 0.00	0.00 ± 0.00
Ashy	Oceanodroma homochroa	0.00 ± 0.00	0.00 ± 0.00	0.00 ± 0.00
Black	Oceanodroma melania	0.00 ± 0.00	0.00 ± 0.00	0.00 ± 0.00
Leach's	Oceanodroma leucorhoa	0.00 ± 0.00	0.00 ± 0.00	0.00 ± 0.00
Tropicbirds	Phaethontidae	0.00 ± 0.00	0.00 ± 0.00	0.00 ± 0.00
Red-billed	Phaethon aethereus	0.00 ± 0.00	0.00 ± 0.00	0.00 ± 0.00
Pelicans	Pelecanidae	1.71 ± 0.43	1.32 ± 0.24	5.19 ± 1.77
Brown	Pelecanus occidentalis	1.71 ± 0.43	1.32 ± 0.24	5.19 ± 1.77
Cormorants	Phalacrocoracidae	0.87 ± 0.18	2.14 ± 0.98	2.54 ± 1.20
Brandt's	Phalacrocorax penicillatus	0.29 ± 0.07	0.38 ± 0.18	0.34 ± 0.12
Double-crested	Phalacrocorax auritus	0.23 ± 0.07	0.24 ± 0.08	0.27 ± 0.09
Pelagic	Phalacrocorax pelagicus	0.01 ± 0.01	0.00 ± 0.00	0.00 ± 0.00
Sea ducks	Anatidae	18.76 ± 9.09	1.48 ± 0.73	0.18 ± 0.15
Brant	Branta bernicla	0.13 ± 0.13	0.00 ± 0.00	0.00 ± 0.00
Red-breasted Merganser	Mergus serrator	0.00 ± 0.00	0.00 ± 0.00	0.00 ± 0.00
Surf Scoter	Melanitta perspicillata	18.62 ± 9.09	1.48 ± 0.73	0.18 ± 0.15
White-winged Scoter	Melanitta fusca	0.01 ± 0.01	0.00 ± 0.00	0.00 ± 0.00

TABLE 3C. CONTINUED.

Species		Southern mainland coastline		
		January	May	September
Larids	Laridae	35.05 ± 11.01	8.23 ± 1.04	29.72 ± 4.37
Gulls	Larinae	34.42 ± 11.01	4.16 ± 0.69	22.48 ± 3.99
Black-legged Kittiwake	Rissa tridactyla	0.00 ± 0.00	0.00 ± 0.00	0.00 ± 0.00
Bonaparte's	Larus philadelphia	0.00 ± 0.00	0.01 ± 0.01	0.00 ± 0.00
California	Larus californicus	20.22 ± 10.50	0.21 ± 0.07	0.27 ± 0.11
Glaucous	Larus hyperboreus	0.00 ± 0.00	0.00 ± 0.00	0.01 ± 0.01
Glaucous-winged	Larus glaucescens	0.03 ± 0.02	0.00 ± 0.00	0.01 ± 0.01
Heermann's	Larus heermanni	0.89 ± 0.19	0.13 ± 0.05	3.78 ± 0.83
Herring	Larus argentatus	0.01 ± 0.01	0.00 ± 0.00	0.00 ± 0.00
Mew	Larus canus	0.13 ± 0.13	0.00 ± 0.00	0.00 ± 0.00
Ring-billed	Larus delawarensis	0.51 ± 0.24	0.00 ± 0.00	0.00 ± 0.00
Sabine's	Xema sabini	0.00 ± 0.00	0.00 ± 0.00	0.00 ± 0.00
Western	Larus occidentalis	8.93 ± 2.87	3.44 ± 0.64	16.00 ± 3.52
Terns	Sterninae	0.62 ± 0.12	4.07 ± 0.62	7.21 ± 1.21
Caspian	Hydroprogne caspia	0.06 ± 0.03	0.67 ± 0.16	1.44 ± 0.39
Common/Arctic	Sterna hirundo/paradisaea	0.00 ± 0.00	0.00 ± 0.00	0.00 ± 0.00
Elegant	Thalasseus elegans	0.04 ± 0.04	0.93 ± 0.23	2.16 ± 0.51
Elegant/Royal	Thalasseus elegans/maximus	0.37 ± 0.09	1.25 ± 0.28	3.25 ± 0.75
Forster's	Sterna forsteri	0.10 ± 0.06	0.48 ± 0.14	0.21 ± 0.11
Least	Sterna antillarum	0.00 ± 0.00	0.44 ± 0.12	0.00 ± 0.00
Royal	Thalasseus maximus	0.00 ± 0.00	0.00 ± 0.00	0.00 ± 0.00
Jaegers and skuas	Stercorariinae	0.00 ± 0.00	0.00 ± 0.00	0.03 ± 0.02
Long-tailed Jaeger	Stercorarius longicaudus	0.00 ± 0.00	0.00 ± 0.00	0.00 ± 0.00
Parasitic Jaegar	Stercorarius parasiticus	0.00 ± 0.00	0.00 ± 0.00	0.03 ± 0.02
Pomarine Jaeger	Stercorarius pomarinus	0.00 ± 0.00	0.00 ± 0.00	0.00 ± 0.00
South Polar Skua	Stercorarius maccormicki	0.00 ± 0.00	0.00 ± 0.00	0.00 ± 0.00
Alcids	Alcidae	0.00 ± 0.00	0.00 ± 0.00	0.00 ± 0.00
Cassin's Auklet	Ptychoramphus aleuticus	0.00 ± 0.00	0.00 ± 0.00	0.00 ± 0.00
Common Murre	Uria aalge	0.00 ± 0.00	0.00 ± 0.00	0.00 ± 0.00
Pigeon Guillemots	Cepphus columba	0.00 ± 0.00	0.00 ± 0.00	0.00 ± 0.00
Rhinoceros Auklet	Cerorhinca monocerata	0.00 ± 0.00	0.00 ± 0.00	0.00 ± 0.00
Xantus's Murrelet	Synthliboramphus hypoleucus	0.00 ± 0.00	0.00 ± 0.00	0.00 ± 0.00
Phalaropes	Phalaropodinae	0.00 ± 0.00	0.00 ± 0.00	0.00 ± 0.00
Red	Phalaropus fulicarius	0.00 ± 0.00	0.00 ± 0.00	0.00 ± 0.00
Red-necked	Phalaropus lobatus	0.00 ± 0.00	0.00 ± 0.00	0.00 ± 0.00

TABLE 4A. DENSITIES (BIRDS/KM² ± SE) OF SEABIRDS FROM COASTAL TRANSECTS AROUND THE NORTHERN CHANNEL ISLANDS' COASTLINES IN THE SOUTHERN CALIFORNIA BIGHT DURING JANUARY, MAY, AND SEPTEMBER FROM 1999–2002. NORTHERN CHANNEL ISLANDS INCLUDE SAN MIGUEL, SANTA ROSA, SANTA CRUZ, AND ANACAPA ISLANDS.

Species	Northern Channel Islands' coastlines		
	January	May	September
All seabirds	82.01 ± 10.58	22.32 ± 2.41	26.77 ± 4.88
Loons Gaviidae	3.96 ± 0.64	0.74 ± 0.21	0.00 ± 0.00
Common *Gavia immer*	0.17 ± 0.05	0.07 ± 0.03	0.00 ± 0.00
Pacific *Gavia pacifica*	2.46 ± 0.38	0.59 ± 0.20	0.00 ± 0.00
Red-throated *Gavia stellata*	0.02 ± 0.02	0.00 ± 0.00	0.00 ± 0.00
Grebes Podicipedidae	0.81 ± 0.53	0.17 ± 0.08	0.03 ± 0.02
Horned *Podiceps auritus*	0.00 ± 0.00	0.00 ± 0.00	0.00 ± 0.00
Pied-billed *Podilymbus podiceps*	0.00 ± 0.00	0.00 ± 0.00	0.00 ± 0.00
Western *Aechmophorus occidentalis*	0.24 ± 0.12	0.17 ± 0.08	0.03 ± 0.02
Albatrosses Diomedeidae	0.00 ± 0.00	0.00 ± 0.00	0.00 ± 0.00
Black-footed *Phoebastria nigripes*	0.00 ± 0.00	0.00 ± 0.00	0.00 ± 0.00
Laysan *Phoebastria immutabilis*	0.00 ± 0.00	0.00 ± 0.00	0.00 ± 0.00
Shearwaters and fulmars Procellariidae	0.05 ± 0.04	0.42 ± 0.23	0.55 ± 0.49
Buller's Shearwater *Puffinus bulleri*	0.00 ± 0.00	0.00 ± 0.00	0.00 ± 0.00
Black-vented Shearwater *Puffinus opisthomelas*	0.00 ± 0.00	0.00 ± 0.00	0.01 ± 0.01
Northern Fulmar *Fulmarus glacialis*	0.01 ± 0.01	0.00 ± 0.00	0.00 ± 0.00
Pink-footed Shearwater *Puffinus creatopus*	0.00 ± 0.00	0.01 ± 0.01	0.04 ± 0.02
Sooty Shearwater *Puffinus griseus*	0.04 ± 0.04	0.28 ± 0.21	0.14 ± 0.11
Storm-Petrels Hydrobatidae	0.00 ± 0.00	0.00 ± 0.00	0.01 ± 0.01
Ashy *Oceanodroma homochroa*	0.00 ± 0.00	0.00 ± 0.00	0.00 ± 0.00
Black *Oceanodroma melania*	0.00 ± 0.00	0.00 ± 0.00	0.01 ± 0.01
Leach's *Oceanodroma leucorhoa*	0.00 ± 0.00	0.00 ± 0.00	0.00 ± 0.00
Tropicbirds Phaethontidae	0.00 ± 0.00	0.00 ± 0.00	0.00 ± 0.00
Red-billed *Phaethon aethereus*	0.00 ± 0.00	0.00 ± 0.00	0.00 ± 0.00
Pelicans Pelecanidae	0.94 ± 0.15	0.91 ± 0.14	3.75 ± 1.98
Brown *Pelecanus occidentalis*	0.94 ± 0.15	0.91 ± 0.14	3.75 ± 1.98
Cormorants Phalacrocoracidae	6.08 ± 1.41	5.15 ± 1.11	7.02 ± 2.08
Brandt's *Phalacrocorax penicillatus*	2.52 ± 0.45	2.83 ± 0.34	2.55 ± 0.58
Double-crested *Phalacrocorax auritus*	0.14 ± 0.03	0.22 ± 0.06	0.18 ± 0.05
Pelagic *Phalacrocorax pelagicus*	0.39 ± 0.06	0.24 ± 0.04	0.00 ± 0.00
Sea ducks Anatidae	14.28 ± 2.39	0.86 ± 0.49	0.00 ± 0.00
Brant *Branta bernicla*	0.00 ± 0.00	0.00 ± 0.00	0.00 ± 0.00
Red-breasted Merganser *Mergus serrator*	0.00 ± 0.00	0.00 ± 0.00	0.00 ± 0.00
Surf Scoter *Melanitta perspicillata*	14.28 ± 2.39	0.86 ± 0.49	0.00 ± 0.00
White-winged Scoter *Melanitta fusca*	0.00 ± 0.00	0.00 ± 0.00	0.00 ± 0.00

TABLE 4A. CONTINUED.

Species		Northern Channel Islands' coastlines		
		January	May	September
Larids	Laridae	54.90 ± 10.33	13.34 ± 1.92	15.09 ± 2.08
Gulls	Larinae	54.64 ± 10.34	13.33 ± 1.92	13.60 ± 2.02
Black-legged Kittiwake	Rissa tridactyla	0.09 ± 0.04	0.00 ± 0.00	0.00 ± 0.00
Bonaparte's	Larus philadelphia	0.00 ± 0.00	0.00 ± 0.00	0.00 ± 0.00
California	Larus californicus	36.92 ± 9.58	0.31 ± 0.11	0.12 ± 0.04
Glaucous	Larus hyperboreus	0.00 ± 0.00	0.00 ± 0.00	0.00 ± 0.00
Glaucous-winged	Larus glaucescens	0.04 ± 0.03	0.00 ± 0.00	0.01 ± 0.01
Heermann's	Larus heermanni	1.30 ± 0.28	0.01 ± 0.01	1.23 ± 0.27
Herring	Larus argentatus	0.00 ± 0.00	0.00 ± 0.00	0.00 ± 0.00
Mew	Larus canus	0.01 ± 0.01	0.00 ± 0.00	0.00 ± 0.00
Ring-billed	Larus delawarensis	0.00 ± 0.00	0.00 ± 0.00	0.00 ± 0.00
Sabine's	Xema sabini	0.00 ± 0.00	0.00 ± 0.00	0.00 ± 0.00
Western	Larus occidentalis	15.32 ± 3.37	12.75 ± 1.86	12.08 ± 1.96
Terns	Sterninae	0.26 ± 0.07	0.01 ± 0.01	1.48 ± 0.66
Caspian	Hydroprogne caspia	0.02 ± 0.02	0.01 ± 0.01	0.08 ± 0.04
Common/Arctic	Sterna hirundo/paradisaea	0.00 ± 0.00	0.00 ± 0.00	0.00 ± 0.00
Elegant	Thalasseus elegans	0.00 ± 0.00	0.00 ± 0.00	0.00 ± 0.00
Elegant/Royal	Thalasseus elegans/maximus	0.07 ± 0.04	0.00 ± 0.00	1.29 ± 0.66
Forster's	Sterna forsteri	0.00 ± 0.00	0.00 ± 0.00	0.00 ± 0.00
Least	Sterna antillarum	0.00 ± 0.00	0.00 ± 0.00	0.00 ± 0.00
Royal	Thalasseus maximus	0.15 ± 0.05	0.00 ± 0.00	0.10 ± 0.04
Jaegers and skuas	Stercorariinae	0.00 ± 0.00	0.00 ± 0.00	0.01 ± 0.01
Long-tailed Jaeger	Stercorarius longicaudus	0.00 ± 0.00	0.00 ± 0.00	0.00 ± 0.00
Parasitic Jaegar	Stercorarius parasiticus	0.00 ± 0.00	0.00 ± 0.00	0.00 ± 0.00
Pomarine Jaeger	Stercorarius pomarinus	0.00 ± 0.00	0.00 ± 0.00	0.01 ± 0.01
South Polar Skua	Stercorarius maccormicki	0.00 ± 0.00	0.00 ± 0.00	0.00 ± 0.00
Alcids	Alcidae	0.35 ± 0.15	0.57 ± 0.10	0.06 ± 0.03
Cassin's Auklet	Ptychoramphus aleuticus	0.24 ± 0.13	0.04 ± 0.02	0.00 ± 0.00
Common Murre	Uria aalge	0.00 ± 0.00	0.00 ± 0.00	0.00 ± 0.00
Pigeon Guillemots	Cepphus columba	0.01 ± 0.01	0.53 ± 0.10	0.04 ± 0.02
Rhinoceros Auklet	Cerorhinca monocerata	0.06 ± 0.04	0.01 ± 0.01	0.00 ± 0.00
Xantus's Murrelet	Synthliboramphus hypoleucus	0.00 ± 0.00	0.00 ± 0.00	0.00 ± 0.00
Phalaropes	Phalaropodinae	0.00 ± 0.00	0.12 ± 0.11	0.10 ± 0.04
Red	Phalaropus fulicarius	0.00 ± 0.00	0.00 ± 0.00	0.00 ± 0.00
Red-necked	Phalaropus lobatus	0.00 ± 0.00	0.01 ± 0.01	0.02 ± 0.02

TABLE 4B. DENSITIES (BIRDS/KM² ± SE) OF SEABIRDS FROM COASTAL TRANSECTS AROUND THE SOUTHERN CHANNEL ISLANDS' COASTLINES IN THE SOUTHERN CALIFORNIA BIGHT DURING JANUARY, MAY, AND SEPTEMBER FROM 1999–2002. SOUTHERN CHANNEL ISLANDS INCLUDE SANTA BARBARA, SAN NICOLAS, SANTA CATALINA, AND SAN CLEMENTE ISLANDS.

Species			Southern Channel Islands' coastlines		
			January	May	September
All seabirds			86.05 ± 15.29	15.52 ± 2.90	17.67 ± 1.98
Loons		Gaviidae	0.35 ± 0.08	0.08 ± 0.08	0.00 ± 0.00
	Common	Gavia immer	0.06 ± 0.04	0.00 ± 0.00	0.00 ± 0.00
	Pacific	Gavia pacifica	0.25 ± 0.07	0.08 ± 0.08	0.00 ± 0.00
	Red-throated	Gavia stellata	0.00 ± 0.00	0.00 ± 0.00	0.00 ± 0.00
Grebes		Podicipedidae	0.03 ± 0.02	0.02 ± 0.02	0.01 ± 0.01
	Horned	Podiceps auritus	0.00 ± 0.00	0.00 ± 0.00	0.00 ± 0.00
	Pied-billed	Podilymbus podiceps	0.00 ± 0.00	0.00 ± 0.00	0.00 ± 0.00
	Western	Aechmophorus occidentalis	0.01 ± 0.01	0.02 ± 0.02	0.01 ± 0.01
Albatrosses		Diomedeidae	0.00 ± 0.00	0.00 ± 0.00	0.00 ± 0.00
	Black-footed	Phoebastria nigripes	0.00 ± 0.00	0.00 ± 0.00	0.00 ± 0.00
	Laysan	Phoebastria immutabilis	0.00 ± 0.00	0.00 ± 0.00	0.00 ± 0.00
Shearwaters and fulmars		Procellariidae	0.00 ± 0.00	0.00 ± 0.00	0.03 ± 0.03
	Buller's Shearwater	Puffinus bulleri	0.00 ± 0.00	0.00 ± 0.00	0.00 ± 0.00
	Black-vented Shearwater	Puffinus opisthomelas	0.00 ± 0.00	0.00 ± 0.00	0.00 ± 0.00
	Northern Fulmar	Fulmarus glacialis	0.00 ± 0.00	0.00 ± 0.00	0.00 ± 0.00
	Pink-footed Shearwater	Puffinus creatopus	0.00 ± 0.00	0.00 ± 0.00	0.00 ± 0.00
	Sooty Shearwater	Puffinus griseus	0.00 ± 0.00	0.00 ± 0.00	0.03 ± 0.03
Storm-Petrels		Hydrobatidae	0.00 ± 0.00	0.00 ± 0.00	0.00 ± 0.00
	Ashy	Oceanodroma homochroa	0.00 ± 0.00	0.00 ± 0.00	0.00 ± 0.00
	Black	Oceanodroma melania	0.00 ± 0.00	0.00 ± 0.00	0.00 ± 0.00
	Leach's	Oceanodroma leucorhoa	0.00 ± 0.00	0.00 ± 0.00	0.00 ± 0.00
Tropicbirds		Phaethontidae	0.00 ± 0.00	0.00 ± 0.00	0.00 ± 0.00
	Red-billed	Phaethon aethereus	0.00 ± 0.00	0.00 ± 0.00	0.00 ± 0.00
Pelicans		Pelecanidae	1.14 ± 0.29	0.59 ± 0.17	1.94 ± 0.49
	Brown	Pelecanus occidentalis	1.14 ± 0.29	0.59 ± 0.17	1.94 ± 0.49
Cormorants		Phalacrocoracidae	2.48 ± 0.30	2.02 ± 0.41	1.46 ± 0.23
	Brandt's	Phalacrocorax penicillatus	1.75 ± 0.24	1.65 ± 0.39	0.91 ± 0.16
	Double-crested	Phalacrocorax auritus	0.16 ± 0.06	0.22 ± 0.07	0.07 ± 0.03
	Pelagic	Phalacrocorax pelagicus	0.03 ± 0.02	0.00 ± 0.00	0.01 ± 0.01
Sea ducks		Anatidae	0.62 ± 0.21	0.00 ± 0.00	0.00 ± 0.00
	Brant	Branta bernicla	0.00 ± 0.00	0.00 ± 0.00	0.00 ± 0.00
	Red-breasted Merganser	Mergus serrator	0.00 ± 0.00	0.00 ± 0.00	0.00 ± 0.00
	Surf Scoter	Melanitta perspicillata	0.62 ± 0.21	0.00 ± 0.00	0.00 ± 0.00
	White-winged Scoter	Melanitta fusca	0.00 ± 0.00	0.00 ± 0.00	0.00 ± 0.00

TABLE 4B. CONTINUED.

Species		Southern Channel Islands' coastlines		
		January	May	September
Larids	Laridae	81.40 ± 15.25	12.69 ± 2.77	14.20 ± 1.73
Gulls	Larinae	78.39 ± 15.18	12.65 ± 2.78	13.94 ± 1.72
Black-legged Kittiwake	*Rissa tridactyla*	0.03 ± 0.02	0.00 ± 0.00	0.00 ± 0.00
Bonaparte's	*Larus philadelphia*	0.00 ± 0.00	0.00 ± 0.00	0.00 ± 0.00
California	*Larus californicus*	59.51 ± 14.43	0.05 ± 0.04	0.15 ± 0.06
Glaucous	*Larus hyperboreus*	0.00 ± 0.00	0.00 ± 0.00	0.00 ± 0.00
Glaucous-winged	*Larus glaucescens*	0.00 ± 0.00	0.02 ± 0.02	0.00 ± 0.00
Heermann's	*Larus heermanni*	5.01 ± 2.43	0.03 ± 0.02	2.33 ± 0.68
Herring	*Larus argentatus*	0.06 ± 0.03	0.00 ± 0.00	0.00 ± 0.00
Mew	*Larus canus*	0.00 ± 0.00	0.00 ± 0.00	0.00 ± 0.00
Ring-billed	*Larus delawarensis*	0.01 ± 0.01	0.00 ± 0.00	0.00 ± 0.00
Sabine's	*Xema sabini*	0.00 ± 0.00	0.00 ± 0.00	0.00 ± 0.00
Western	*Larus occidentalis*	12.67 ± 3.64	12.50 ± 2.77	11.07 ± 1.48
Terns	Sterninae	3.01 ± 2.26	0.02 ± 0.02	0.27 ± 0.11
Caspian	*Hydroprogne caspia*	0.00 ± 0.00	0.00 ± 0.00	0.04 ± 0.03
Common/Arctic	*Sterna hirundo/paradisaea*	0.00 ± 0.00	0.00 ± 0.00	0.00 ± 0.00
Elegant	*Thalasseus elegans*	0.00 ± 0.00	0.00 ± 0.00	0.00 ± 0.00
Elegant/Royal	*Thalasseus elegans/maximus*	2.93 ± 2.26	0.02 ± 0.02	0.17 ± 0.10
Forster's	*Sterna forsteri*	0.00 ± 0.00	0.00 ± 0.00	0.00 ± 0.00
Least	*Sterna antillarum*	0.00 ± 0.00	0.00 ± 0.00	0.00 ± 0.00
Royal	*Thalasseus maximus*	0.07 ± 0.04	0.00 ± 0.00	0.04 ± 0.03
Jaegers and skuas	Stercorariinae	0.00 ± 0.00	0.02 ± 0.02	0.00 ± 0.00
Long-tailed Jaeger	*Stercorarius longicaudus*	0.00 ± 0.00	0.02 ± 0.02	0.00 ± 0.00
Parasitic Jaegar	*Stercorarius parasiticus*	0.00 ± 0.00	0.00 ± 0.00	0.00 ± 0.00
Pomarine Jaeger	*Stercorarius pomarinus*	0.00 ± 0.00	0.00 ± 0.00	0.00 ± 0.00
South Polar Skua	*Stercorarius maccormicki*	0.00 ± 0.00	0.00 ± 0.00	0.00 ± 0.00
Alcids	Alcidae	0.01 ± 0.01	0.08 ± 0.05	0.03 ± 0.03
Cassin's Auklet	*Ptychoramphus aleuticus*	0.00 ± 0.00	0.00 ± 0.00	0.00 ± 0.00
Common Murre	*Uria aalge*	0.01 ± 0.01	0.00 ± 0.00	0.00 ± 0.00
Pigeon Guillemots	*Cepphus columba*	0.00 ± 0.00	0.08 ± 0.05	0.03 ± 0.03
Rhinoceros Auklet	*Cerorhinca monocerata*	0.00 ± 0.00	0.00 ± 0.00	0.00 ± 0.00
Xantus's Murrelet	*Synthliboramphus hypoleucus*	0.00 ± 0.00	0.00 ± 0.00	0.00 ± 0.00
Phalaropes	Phalaropodinae	0.01 ± 0.01	0.02 ± 0.02	0.00 ± 0.00
Red	*Phalaropus fulicarius*	0.01 ± 0.01	0.00 ± 0.00	0.00 ± 0.00
Red-necked	*Phalaropus lobatus*	0.00 ± 0.00	0.00 ± 0.00	0.00 ± 0.00

TABLE 5. SIGNIFICANCE TESTS BASED ON F-STATISTICS FROM THE GLMM MODEL FOR ANALYZING SEASON, SUB-AREA, AND SEASON-BY-SUB-AREA INTERACTION EFFECTS ON AT-SEA DENSITIES OF SEABIRDS BY SPECIES. ALL TESTS WERE CONDUCTED FOR THE RANGE OF MONTHS AND SUB-AREAS HAVING A POSITIVE DENSITY ESTIMATE. DIFFERENCES AMONG ALL MONTHS (JANUARY, MAY, AND SEPTEMBER) AND ALL SUB-AREAS (S1 THROUGH S5) WERE TESTED, UNLESS OTHERWISE NOTED. SPECIES TYPES WITH NO TEST FOR A SEASON, SUB-AREA, OR INTERACTION EFFECT DID NOT HAVE SUFFICIENT DENSITY INFORMATION TO TEST THAT EFFECT. ANY EFFECT WITH F-STATISTIC LEADING TO A P < 0.05 IS CONSIDERED TO BE STATISTICALLY SIGNIFICANT.

Species		Seasons and subareas used (all months and subareas unless noted)	Season	Subarea	Interaction
All seabirds			$F_{2,4932} = 0.8$; P = 0.451	$F_{4,4932} = 22.1$; P < 0.001	$F_{8,4932} = 1.4$; P = 0.176
Loons	Gaviidae				
Common	Gavia immer	S1, S3, S4, and S5	$F_{2,4487} = 6.2$; P = 0.002	$F_{3,4487} = 4.5$; P = 0.004	
Pacific	Gavia pacifica	Jan and May; S1 and S3	$F_{1,1335} = 3.1$; P = 0.077	$F_{1,1335} = 0.0$; P = 0.950	
Western Grebe	Aechmophorus occidentalis	Jan and May; S1, S3, S4, and S5	$F_{1,3038} = 3.7$; P = 0.055	$F_{3,3038} = 1.7$; P = 0.160	
Shearwaters and fulmars	Procellariidae	S1, S3, and S4	$F_{2,3266} = 0.8$; P = 0.431	$F_{2,3266} = 1.1$; P = 0.322	$F_{4,3266} = 0.9$; P = 0.442
Black-vented Shearwater	Puffinus opisthomelas	S1, S3, S4, and S5	$F_{2,4932} = 5.9$; P = 0.003	$F_{4,4932} = 3.7$; P = 0.005	$F_{8,4932} = 1.4$; P = 0.191
Northern Fulmar	Fulmarus glacialis		$F_{2,4487} = 3.1$; P = 0.046	$F_{3,4487} = 2.9$; P = 0.032	
Pink-footed Shearwater	Puffinus creatopus		$F_{2,4940} = 49.1$; P < 0.001	$F_{4,4940} = 5.1$; P < 0.001	
Sooty Shearwater	Puffinus griseus		$F_{2,4932} = 12.3$; P < 0.001	$F_{4,4932} = 0.8$; P = 0.495	$F_{8,4932} = 0.7$; P = 0.734
Ashy Storm-Petrel	Oceanodroma homochroa		$F_{2,4940} = 14.4$; P < 0.001	$F_{4,4940} = 16.5$; P < 0.001	
Black Storm-Petrel	Oceanodroma melania		$F_{2,4940} = 4.3$; P = 0.013	$F_{4,4940} = 5.2$; P < 0.001	
Leach's Storm-Petrel	Oceanodroma leucorhoa		$F_{2,4940} = 5.6$; P = 0.004	$F_{4,4940} = 2.5$; P = 0.040	
Brown Pelican	Pelecanus occidentalis		$F_{2,4940} = 17.1$; P < 0.001	$F_{4,4940} = 25.4$; P < 0.001	
Cormorants	Phalacrocoracidae	S1, S3, S4, and S5	$F_{2,4940} = 9.4$; P < 0.001	$F_{4,4940} = 6.2$; P < 0.001	
Brandt's	Phalacrocorax penicillatus	S1, S3, S4, and S5	$F_{2,4481} = 0.9$; P = 0.409	$F_{3,4481} = 7.0$; P < 0.001	$F_{6,4481} = 2.0$; P = 0.060
Double-crested	Phalacrocorax auritus	S1, S3, S4, and S5	$F_{2,4481} = 0.3$; P = 0.734	$F_{3,4481} = 5.6$; P < 0.001	$F_{6,4481} = 1.0$; P = 0.427
Surf Scoter	Melanitta perspicillata	Jan and May; S1 and S3	$F_{2,4487} = 4.5$; P = 0.012; $F_{1,1335} = 2.1$; P = 0.146	$F_{3,4487} = 7.3$; P < 0.001; $F_{1,1335} = 2.1$; P = 0.145	
Larids	Laridae		$F_{2,4932} = 4.1$; P = 0.017	$F_{4,4932} = 12.7$; P < 0.001	$F_{8,4932} = 1.2$; P = 0.295
Black-legged Kittiwake	Rissa tridactyla	Jan and May	$F_{1,3363} = 29.8$; P < 0.001	$F_{4,4363} = 2.1$; P = 0.082	
Bonaparte's Gull	Larus philadelphia	Jan and May	$F_{1,3362} = 7.8$; P = 0.005	$F_{4,4362} = 3.6$; P = 0.006	
California Gull	Larus californicus		$F_{2,4940} = 22.2$; P < 0.001	$F_{4,4940} = 6.3$; P < 0.001	
Heermann's Gull	Larus heermanni	Jan and Sep; S1, S3, S4, and S5	$F_{1,2950} = 0.1$; P = 0.721	$F_{3,2950} = 6.5$; P < 0.001	$F_{3,2950} = 1.8$; P = 0.149
Sabine's Gull	Xema sabini	May and Sep	$F_{1,3262} = 1.3$; P = 0.259	$F_{4,3262} = 17.3$; P < 0.001	$F_{4,3262} = 0.9$; P = 0.467
Western Gull	Larus occidentalis		$F_{2,4932} = 0.0$; P = 0.968	$F_{4,4932} = 21.9$; P < 0.001	$F_{4,3262} = 1.2$; P = 0.284
Alcids	Alcidae		$F_{2,4933} = 26.3$; P < 0.001	$F_{4,4933} = 6.7$; P < 0.001	$F_{8,4933} = 4.9$; P < 0.001
Cassin's Auklet	Ptychoramphus aleuticus		$F_{2,4940} = 13.3$; P < 0.001	$F_{4,4940} = 10.7$; P < 0.001	
Common Murre	Uria aalge	S1, S3, and S4	$F_{2,3270} = 8.0$; P < 0.001	$F_{2,3270} = 27.8$; P < 0.001	
Rhinoceros Auklet	Cerorhinca monocerata		$F_{2,4940} = 73.6$; P < 0.001	$F_{4,4940} = 22.7$; P < 0.001	
Xantus's Murrelet	Synthliboramphus hypoleucus		$F_{2,4940} = 15.4$; P < 0.001	$F_{4,4940} = 0.5$; P = 0.700	
Phalaropes	Phalaropodinae		$F_{2,4940} = 6.3$; P = 0.002	$F_{4,4932} = 8.1$; P < 0.001	$F_{8,4932} = 3.0$; P = 0.002
Red	Phalaropus fulicarius		$F_{2,4932} = 10.6$; P < 0.001	$F_{4,4932} = 8.5$; P < 0.001	$F_{8,4932} = 3.3$; P < 0.001
Red-necked	Phalaropus lobatus		$F_{2,4932} = 17.8$; P < 0.001	$F_{4,4932} = 1.2$; P = 0.295	$F_{8,4932} = 1.8$; P = 0.080

TABLE 6. SIGNIFICANCE TESTS BASED ON F-STATISTICS FROM THE GLMM MODEL FOR ANALYZING SEASON, SUB-AREA, AND SEASON-BY-SUB-AREA INTERACTION EFFECTS ON COASTAL DENSITIES OF SEABIRDS BY SPECIES. ALL TESTS WERE CONDUCTED FOR THE RANGE OF MONTHS AND SUB-AREAS HAVING A POSITIVE DENSITY ESTIMATE. DIFFERENCES AMONG ALL MONTHS (JANUARY, MAY, AND SEPTEMBER) AND ALL SUB-AREAS (NIC = NORTHERN ISLAND COASTLINE, SIC = SOUTHERN ISLAND COASTLINE, NMC = NORTHERN MAINLAND COASTLINE, CMC = CENTRAL MAINLAND COASTLINE, AND SMC = SOUTHERN MAINLAND COASTLINE) WERE TESTED, UNLESS OTHERWISE NOTED. SPECIES TYPES WITH NO TEST FOR A SEASON, SUB-AREA, OR INTERACTION EFFECT DID NOT HAVE SUFFICIENT DENSITY INFORMATION TO TEST THAT EFFECT. ANY EFFECT WITH F-STATISTIC LEADING TO A P < 0.05 IS CONSIDERED TO BE STATISTICALLY SIGNIFICANT.

Species		Seasons and subareas used (all months and subareas unless noted)	Season	Subarea	Interaction
All seabirds			$F_{2,1781} = 13.5; P < 0.001$	$F_{4,1781} = 5.4; P < 0.001$	$F_{8,1781} = 3.9; P < 0.001$
Loons	*Gaviidae*		$F_{2,1789} = 57.6; P < 0.001$	$F_{4,1789} = 8.5; P < 0.001$	
Common	*Gavia immer*		$F_{2,1789} = 9.9; P < 0.001$	$F_{4,1789} = 3.8; P = 0.005$	
Pacific	*Gavia pacifica*		$F_{2,1789} = 22.9; P < 0.001$	$F_{4,1789} = 10.5; P < 0.001$	
Western Grebe	*Aechmophorus occidentalis*		$F_{2,1781} = 0.1; P = 0.896$	$F_{4,1781} = 6.1; P < 0.001$	$F_{8,1781} = 1.5; P = 0.156$
Shearwaters and fulmars	*Procellariidae*	NIC, SIC, CMC, and NMC	$F_{2,1436} = 1.0; P = 0.380$	$F_{3,1436} = 1.2; P = 0.306$	
Sooty Shearwater	*Puffinus griseus*	NIC, SIC, CMC, and NMC	$F_{2,1436} = 1.5; P = 0.222$	$F_{3,1436} = 1.5; P = 0.219$	
Brown Pelican	*Pelecanus occidentalis*		$F_{2,1781} = 12.3; P < 0.001$	$F_{4,1781} = 2.0; P = 0.091$	$F_{8,1781} = 1.6; P = 0.135$
Cormorants	*Phalacrocoracidae*		$F_{2,1781} = 0.6; P = 0.549$	$F_{4,1781} = 10.1; P < 0.001$	$F_{8,1781} = 1.4; P = 0.184$
Brandt's	*Phalacrocorax penicillatus*		$F_{2,1781} = 2.2; P = 0.107$	$F_{4,1781} = 23.7; P < 0.001$	$F_{8,1781} = 1.5; P = 0.162$
Double-crested	*Phalacrocorax auritus*		$F_{2,1781} = 0.0; P = 0.953$	$F_{4,1781} = 25.3; P < 0.001$	$F_{8,1781} = 2.1; P = 0.035$
Pelagic	*Phalacrocorax pelagicus*		$F_{2,1789} = 14.6; P < 0.001$	$F_{4,1789} = 14.9; P < 0.001$	
Surf Scoter	*Melanitta perspicillata*		$F_{2,1789} = 36.9; P < 0.001$	$F_{4,1789} = 10.5; P < 0.001$	
Larids	*Laridae*		$F_{2,1781} = 23.2; P < 0.001$	$F_{4,1781} = 1.3; P = 0.281$	$F_{8,1781} = 2.5; P = 0.011$
Bonaparte's Gull	*Larus philadelphia*	Jan and May; CMC and SMC	$F_{1,589} = 0.2; P = 0.664$	$F_{1,589} = 2.0; P = 0.161$	
California Gull	*Larus californicus*		$F_{2,1781} = 12.3; P < 0.001$	$F_{4,1781} = 0.4; P = 0.840$	$F_{8,1781} = 0.7; P = 0.692$
Heermann's Gull	*Larus heermanni*		$F_{2,1781} = 16.1; P < 0.001$	$F_{4,1781} = 0.2; P = 0.921$	$F_{8,1781} = 4.3; P < 0.001$
Western Gull	*Larus occidentalis*		$F_{2,1781} = 4.1; P = 0.016$	$F_{4,1781} = 1.6; P = 0.163$	$F_{8,1781} = 1.6; P = 0.117$
Caspian Tern	*Hydroprogne caspia*		$F_{2,1781} = 33.0; P < 0.001$	$F_{4,1789} = 24.0; P < 0.001$	
Alcids	*Alcidae*	NIC, SIC, CMC, and NMC	$F_{2,1436} = 12.3; P < 0.001$	$F_{3,1436} = 10.0; P < 0.001$	
Cassin's Auklet	*Ptychoramphus aleuticus*	Jan and May; NIC	$F_{1,310} = 4.9; P = 0.027$		
Common Murre	*Uria aalge*	Jan; SIC, CMC, and NMC		$F_{2,333} = 1.9; P = 0.154$	
Pigeon Guillemot	*Cepphus columba*	NIC, SIC, and NMC	$F_{2,927} = 20.5; P < 0.001$	$F_{2,927} = 6.1; P = 0.002$	

TABLE 7A. SIGNIFICANCE TESTS BASED ON WALD'S Z-STATISTICS FROM THE GLM MODEL FOR ANALYZING DIFFERENCES IN AT-SEA DENSITIES OF SEABIRDS BETWEEN 1975–1983 AND 1999–2002, BY SPECIES AND SUB-AREA (S1, S2, AND ALL FIVE SUB-AREAS COMBINED). SPECIES WITH NO TEST FOR A SUB-AREA DID NOT HAVE SUFFICIENT DENSITY INFORMATION TO TEST PERIOD DIFFERENCES IN THAT SUB-AREA. A NEGATIVE Z-STATISTIC INDICATES DENSITIES WERE GREATER FROM 1975–1983. A POSITIVE Z-STATISTIC INDICATES DENSITIES WERE GREATER FROM 1999–2002. ANY EFFECT WITH A $P < 0.05$ IS CONSIDERED TO BE STATISTICALLY SIGNIFICANT.

Species		Sub-area		
		All combined	S1	S2
All seabirds		$Z = -12.5; P <0.001$	$Z = -1.3; P = 0.182$	$Z = -2.3; P = 0.024$
Loons	*Gaviidae*	$Z = -5.0; P <0.001$	$Z = 0.4; P = 0.690$	
Common	*Gavia immer*	$Z = -11.5; P <0.001$		
Pacific	*Gavia pacifica*	$Z = -8.8; P <0.001$		
Shearwaters and fulmars	*Procellariidae*	$Z = -3.3; P = 0.001$	$Z = 1.6; P = 0.110$	
Northern Fulmar	*Fulmarus glacialis*	$Z = -6.1; P <0.001$	$Z = -0.1; P = 0.886$	$Z = -5.4; P <0.001$
Pink-footed Shearwater	*Puffinus creatopus*	$Z = -0.4; P = 0.703$	$Z = -0.0; P = 0.976$	$Z = -0.7; P = 0.489$
Sooty Shearwater	*Puffinus griseus*	$Z = 0.3; P = 0.740$	$Z = 1.3; P = 0.186$	$Z = -8.2; P <0.001$
Ashy Storm-Petrel	*Oceanodroma homochroa*	$Z = 16.8; P <0.001$	$Z = 0.6; P = 0.560$	$Z = -7.4; P <0.001$
Black Storm-Petrel	*Oceanodroma melania*	$Z = 9.1; P <0.001$	$Z = 7.6; P <0.001$	$Z = 4.1; P <0.001$
Leach's Storm-Petrel	*Oceanodroma leucorhoa*	$Z = -10.0; P <0.001$	$Z = -4.6; P <0.001$	$Z = -6.3; P <0.001$
Brown Pelican	*Pelecanus occidentalis*	$Z = 4.4; P <0.001$	$Z = -5.2; P <0.001$	$Z = -9.9; P <0.001$
Cormorants	*Phalacrocoracidae*	$Z = 4.1; P <0.001$	$Z = -1.0; P = 0.330$	
Brandt's	*Phalacrocorax penicillatus*	$Z = 13.0; P <0.001$	$Z = 3.5; P <0.001$	
Double-crested	*Phalacrocorax auritus*	$Z = 16.4; P <0.001$	$Z = 4.4; P <0.001$	
Larids	*Laridae*	$Z = -9.7; P <0.001$	$Z = -2.3; P = 0.019$	$Z = -0.9; P = 0.373$
Black-legged Kittiwake	*Rissa tridactyla*	$Z = -8.0; P <0.001$	$Z = -2.1; P = 0.037$	$Z = 3.9; P <0.001$
Bonaparte's Gull	*Larus philadelphia*	$Z = -20.2; P <0.001$	$Z = -7.6; P <0.001$	$Z = -4.8; P <0.001$
California Gull	*Larus californicus*	$Z = -2.4; P = 0.015$	$Z = -1.3; P = 0.182$	$Z = -6.0; P <0.001$
Heermann's Gull	*Larus heermanni*	$Z = -73.4; P <0.001$	$Z = -6.6; P <0.001$	
Sabine's Gull	*Xema sabini*	$Z = 14.8; P <0.001$	$Z = 16.6; P <0.001$	$Z = 3.8; P <0.001$
Western Gull	*Larus occidentalis*	$Z = 3.4; P <0.001$	$Z = -0.7; P = 0.486$	$Z = -2.8; P = 0.005$
Alcids	*Alcidae*	$Z = -11.2; P <0.001$	$Z = -2.0; P = 0.050$	$Z = -3.1; P = 0.002$
Cassin's Auklet	*Ptychoramphus aleuticus*	$Z = -4.8; P <0.001$	$Z = -3.0; P = 0.003$	$Z = -1.9; P = 0.062$
Common Murre	*Uria aalge*	$Z = -17.0; P <0.001$	$Z = -2.3; P = 0.023$	$Z = -6.6; P <0.001$
Rhinoceros Auklet	*Cerorhinca monocerata*	$Z = -3.1; P = 0.002$	$Z = 2.8; P = 0.005$	
Xantus's Murrelet	*Synthliboramphus hypoleucus*	$Z = 3.2; P = 0.002$	$Z = 13.2; P <0.001$	
Phalaropes	*Phalaropodinae*	$Z = -10.2; P <0.001$	$Z = -0.9; P = 0.385$	
Red Phalarope	*Phalaropus fulicarius*	$Z = 5.1; P <0.001$	$Z = 11.6; P <0.001$	$Z = 0.1; P = 0.957$
Red-necked Phalarope	*Phalaropus lobatus*	$Z = 17.6; P <0.001$	$Z = 19.2; P <0.001$	$Z = 5.2; P <0.001$

TABLE 7B. SIGNIFICANCE TESTS BASED ON WALD'S Z-STATISTICS FROM THE GLM MODEL FOR ANALYZING DIFFERENCES IN AT-SEA DENSITIES OF SEABIRDS BETWEEN 1975–1983 AND 1999–2002, BY SPECIES AND SUB-AREA (S3, S4, AND S5). SPECIES WITH NO TEST FOR A SUB-AREA DID NOT HAVE SUFFICIENT DENSITY INFORMATION TO TEST PERIOD DIFFERENCES IN THAT SUB-AREA. A NEGATIVE Z-STATISTIC INDICATES DENSITIES WERE GREATER FROM 1975–1983. A POSITIVE Z-STATISTIC INDICATES DENSITIES WERE GREATER FROM 1999–2002. ANY EFFECT WITH A P < 0.05 IS CONSIDERED TO BE STATISTICALLY SIGNIFICANT.

Species		Sub-area S3	S4	S5
All seabirds		$Z = -0.1$; $P = 0.942$	$Z = -8.7$; $P <0.001$	$Z = -12.7$; $P <0.001$
Loons	Gaviidae	$Z = -10.6$; $P <0.001$	$Z = -11.8$; $P <0.001$	$Z = -13.9$; $P <0.001$
Common	*Gavia immer*	$Z = -9.0$; $P <0.001$		
Pacific	*Gavia pacifica*	$Z = -7.0$; $P <0.001$		
Shearwaters and fulmars	Procellariidae	$Z = 2.9$; $P = 0.004$	$Z = -2.9$; $P = 0.004$	$Z = -14.3$; $P <0.001$
Northern Fulmar	*Fulmarus glacialis*	$Z = -2.8$; $P = 0.005$	$Z = -2.4$; $P = 0.015$	$Z = -2.9$; $P = 0.004$
Pink-footed Shearwater	*Puffinus creatopus*	$Z = -1.1$; $P = 0.284$	$Z = -8.6$; $P <0.001$	$Z = 4.2$; $P <0.001$
Sooty Shearwater	*Puffinus griseus*	$Z = 5.7$; $P <0.001$	$Z = 3.2$; $P = 0.001$	$Z = -16.2$; $P <0.001$
Ashy Strorm-Petrel	*Oceanodroma homochroa*	$Z = 5.7$; $P <0.001$	$Z = -13.9$; $P <0.001$	$Z = -4.9$; $P <0.001$
Black Storm-Petrel	*Oceanodroma melania*	$Z = 4.5$; $P <0.001$	$Z = 6.4$; $P <0.001$	$Z = 4.5$; $P <0.001$
Leach's Storm-Petrel	*Oceanodroma leucorhoa*	$Z = -10.8$; $P <0.001$	$Z = 6.7$; $P <0.001$	$Z = 4.5$; $P <0.001$
Brown Pelican	*Pelecanus occidentalis*	$Z = 1.9$; $P = 0.059$	$Z = -11.3$; $P <0.001$	$Z = -13.0$; $P <0.001$
Cormorants	Phalacrocoracidae	$Z = -11.0$; $P <0.001$	$Z = -2.1$; $P = 0.039$	$Z = 4.1$; $P <0.001$
Brandt's	*Phalacrocorax penicillatus*	$Z = 6.1$; $P <0.001$	$Z = -4.7$; $P <0.001$	$Z = 6.0$; $P <0.001$
Double-crested	*Phalacrocorax auritus*	$Z = 5.9$; $P <0.001$	$Z = 2.0$; $P = 0.047$	$Z = -14.8$; $P <0.001$
Larids	Laridae	$Z = -3.5$; $P <0.001$	$Z = -2.6$; $P = 0.011$	$Z = -1.9$; $P = 0.052$
Black-legged Kittiwake	*Rissa tridactyla*	$Z = -7.5$; $P <0.001$	$Z = -4.0$; $P <0.001$	$Z = -16.0$; $P <0.001$
Bonaparte's Gull	*Larus philadelphia*	$Z = -3.4$; $P <0.001$	$Z = -5.7$; $P <0.001$	$Z = -4.4$; $P <0.001$
California Gull	*Larus californicus*	$Z = -1.9$; $P = 0.057$	$Z = -3.8$; $P <0.001$	$Z = -8.6$; $P <0.001$
Heermann's Gull	*Larus heermanni*	$Z = 3.8$; $P <0.001$	$Z = 0.6$; $P = 0.546$	
Sabine's Gull	*Xema sabini*	$Z = 3.2$; $P = 0.001$	$Z = -10.4$; $P <0.001$	
Western Gull	*Larus occidentalis*	$Z = 2.0$; $P = 0.042$	$Z = 5.2$; $P <0.001$	$Z = -3.1$; $P = 0.002$
Alcids	Alcidae	$Z = -1.3$; $P = 0.187$	$Z = -2.5$; $P = 0.014$	$Z = -5.1$; $P <0.001$
Cassin's Auklet	*Ptychoramphus aleuticus*	$Z = 3.0$; $P = 0.003$	$Z = -4.1$; $P <0.001$	$Z = 8.0$; $P <0.001$
Common Murre	*Uria aalge*	$Z = -14.6$; $P <0.001$	$Z = 3.0$; $P = 0.003$	
Rhinoceros Auklet	*Cerorhinca monocerata*	$Z = -10.7$; $P <0.001$	$Z = -10.5$; $P <0.001$	$Z = -1.1$; $P = 0.290$
Xantus's Murrelet	*Synthliboramphus hypoleucus*	$Z = -0.0$; $P = 0.993$	$Z = 0.4$; $P = 0.653$	$Z = 4.5$; $P <0.001$
Phalaropes	Phalaropodinae	$Z = -4.1$; $P <0.001$	$Z = -1.0$; $P = 0.316$	$Z = -4.2$; $P <0.001$
Red	*Phalaropus fulicarius*	$Z = -8.2$; $P <0.001$	$Z = -2.1$; $P = 0.039$	$Z = 7.7$; $P <0.001$
Red-necked	*Phalaropus lobatus*	$Z = 4.3$; $P <0.001$	$Z = -2.8$; $P = 0.005$	

in S3 in January and in S1 in May (Tables 1, 5). Densities along coastal transects differed among seasons with greatest densities in January and lowest densities in May (Tables 2–4, 6). At-sea densities for all seabirds combined were greater in 1975–1983 than in 1999–2002 for the entire study area, S2, S4, and S5, but did not differ significantly in S1 and S3 (Tables 7a, 7b).

SPECIES ACCOUNTS

GAVIIDAE

Loons occurred commonly in southern California and were observed primarily along mainland and island coastlines (Fig. 6). Because it was difficult to distinguish between Common and Pacific loons (*Gavia immer* and *G. pacifica*), and also some Red-throated Loons (*G. stellata*) when in winter plumage, 52% of loons counted were recorded as unidentified (Fig. 7). At-sea densities differed among seasons and the four sub-areas in which loons occurred (S1, S3, S4, and S5; Table 5). Greatest densities occurred in S3 in January and in S1 in May (Tables 1a, 1c). Coastal densities differed among seasons and sub-areas (Table 6). Greatest coastal densities occurred in January along mainland coasts (Tables 2–4). At-sea densities of loons were greater in 1975–1983 than in 1999–2002 for the entire study area, S2, S3, S4, and S5 (Tables 7a, 7b).

Common Loon

Common Loons winter inshore from the western Aleutian Islands, Alaska, to the southwest coast of Mexico (McIntyre and Barr 1997). In 1975–1983, Common Loons occurred in California waters from late March to late May and from late October to December (Briggs et al. 1987). Briggs et al. (1987) estimated several thousand Common Loons off California in April with hundreds occurring <0.5 km from shore. Most large loon concentrations in 1975–1983 were north of our study area (Briggs et al. 1987). In 1999–2002, we observed loons along the coast near Morro Bay, from Point Arguello to Point Dume, near San Diego, and near San Miguel and Santa Rosa islands in January and May (Fig. 8).

At-sea densities of Common Loons did not differ among the two seasons (January and May) or two sub-areas (S1 and S3) in which they were observed (Table 5). Most (82%) Common Loons were observed on coastal transects. Coastal densities differed among seasons and sub-areas and were greatest in January and along the northern portion of the mainland coast (Tables 2–4, 6).

At-sea densities of Common Loons in 1975–1983 were greater than in 1999–2002 for the entire study area and S3 (Tables 7a, 7b); but since Common Loons occurred mainly in coastal transect areas that were not surveyed by Briggs et al. (1987), we cannot determine if reduced densities truly reflect lower population sizes. In other sub-areas, we lacked the data to make statistical comparisons to Briggs et al. (1987).

Pacific Loon

Pacific Loons, the most abundant loons in North America, are strictly marine except when breeding in the Arctic and sub-Arctic (Russell 2002). Pacific Loons winter from Alaska to Mazatlan, Mexico (Russell 2002). Briggs et al. (1987) recorded greatest abundances off southern California in mid-December, especially within the eastern Santa Barbara Channel northeast of Anacapa Island. In our surveys, Pacific Loons were most common within 40 km of the southern California mainland in all seasons. In 1999–2002, we observed loons in January and May near the northern Channel Islands (except Anacapa) from Point Conception to Point Buchon, between Santa Barbara and Point Dume, and on the west side of Santa Catalina Island (Fig. 9). On at-sea transects, 87% of observed Pacific Loons were <5 km from shore.

In 1999–2002, at-sea densities of Pacific Loons did not differ among the two seasons (January and May) or the four sub-areas (S1, S3, S4, and S5) in which they were observed (Table 5). On coastal transects, densities differed among seasons and sub-areas (Table 6). Coastal densities were greatest in January and along the northern mainland and northern Channel Island coastlines (Tables 2–4).

At-sea densities of Pacific Loons were greater in 1975–1983 than in 1999–2002 for the entire study area, S3, S4, and S5 but did not differ significantly in S1 (Tables 7a, 7b). D. Nysewander (unpubl. data) found a 79% decline for loons in Puget Sound over a 20-yr period, indicating that the reduction in loon abundance may extend along the entire Pacific coast.

WESTERN GREBE (*AECHMOPHORUS OCCIDENTALIS*) AND CLARK'S GREBE (*A. CLARKIA*)

We were unable to distinguish between Western and Clark's grebes from the air, but because most observations indicate that the overwhelming majority are Western Grebes, we combined both species for analyses and hereafter refer to them as Western Grebes. Western Grebes breed on lakes from northwestern Canada to northern Baja California, Mexico,

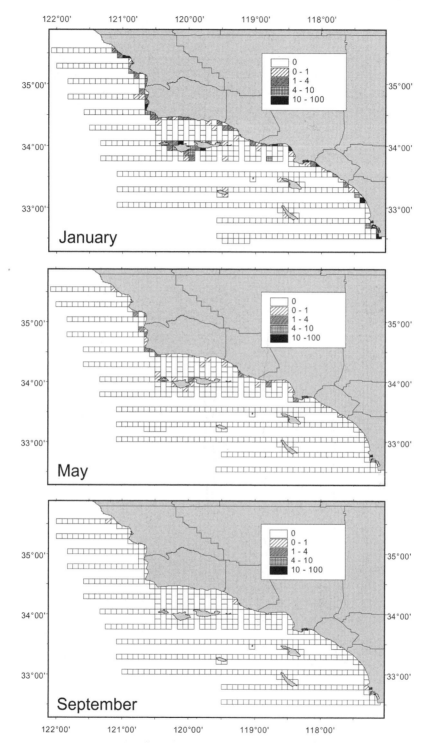

FIGURE 6. Loon densities (birds/km²) and distribution off southern California from 1999–2002 during January, May, and September.

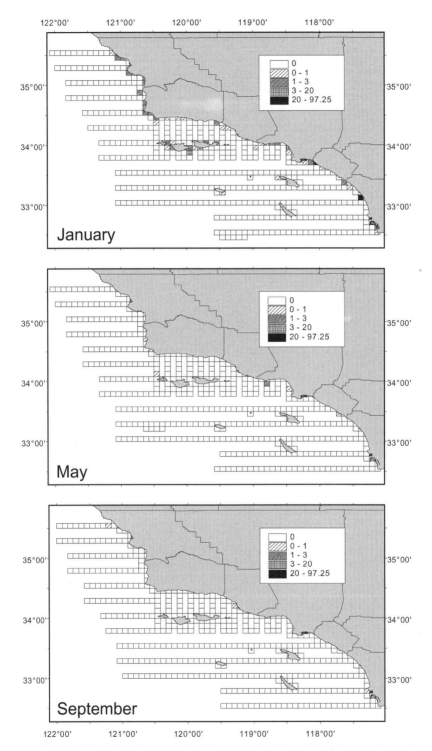

FIGURE 7. Unidentified loon densities (birds/km²) and distribution off southern California from 1999–2002 during January, May, and September.

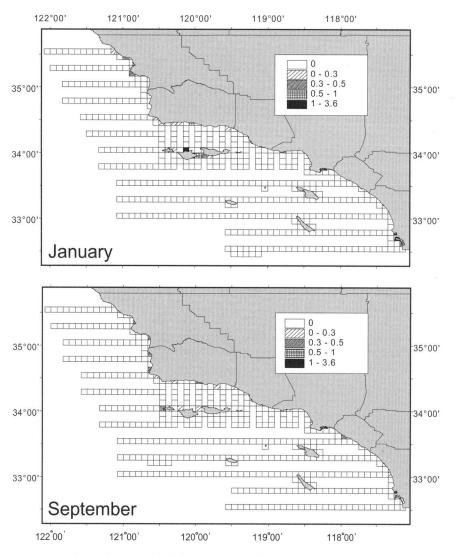

FIGURE 8. Common Loon densities (birds/km²) and distribution off southern California from 1999–2002 during January and September. No Common Loons were observed during May.

and east to Minnesota (Storer and Nuechterlein 1992). Along the Pacific Coast, they winter from southern British Columbia, Canada to southern Baja California, and Sinaloa, Mexico (Storer and Nuechterlein 1992). In the SCB from 1975–1978, Western Grebes were abundant from October through May in the eastern Santa Barbara Channel but rare near the Channel Islands and offshore (Briggs et al. 1987). In 1999–2002, Western Grebes were distributed along mainland and island coasts throughout the study area and we consistently observed aggregations of grebes in all survey months near Morro Bay, Point Sal, and Palos Verdes, and from 75 km north of San Diego to the Mexican border (Fig. 10).

More than 90% of Western Grebes occurred on coastal transects along mainland coasts. At-sea density comparisons were not statistically significant for season or among the three sub-areas where they occurred (S1, S3, and S4; Table 5). In 1999–2002, densities of Western Grebes on coastal transects did not differ among seasons but did differ among sub-areas (Table 6). Greatest densities occurred in NMC in January, SMC in May, and CMC in September (Tables 2–4).

Excluding one aggregation of 1,000 Western Grebes observed 4 km offshore, >70% of Western Grebes observed on at-sea transects occurred <2 km from shore. Therefore, we did

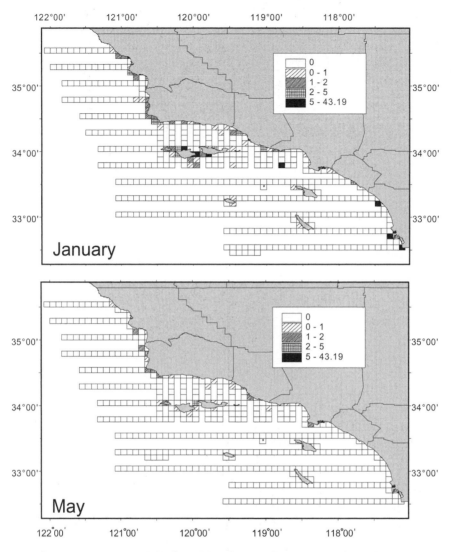

FIGURE 9. Pacific Loon densities (birds/km²) and distribution off southern California from 1999–2002 during January and May. No Pacific Loons were observed during September.

not compare densities statistically with Briggs et al. (1987) who did not conduct aerial coastal transects in the SCB.

PROCELLARIIDAE

We observed ten species of procellariids in the study area (Fig. 11). At-sea densities differed among seasons and sub-areas with greatest densities occurring in January in S1 and in May in S3 (Tables 1, 5). Coastal densities of procellariids did not differ among seasons or four sub-areas in which they occurred but few occurred in coastal habitats (NMC, CMC, NIC, and SIC; Table 6). At-sea densities were greater

in 1975–1983 than in 1999–2002 for the entire study area, S2, S4, and S5; lower in S3; and did not differ significantly in S1 (Tables 7a, 7b).

Black-footed Albatross (Phoebastria nigripes)

The Black-footed Albatross is the most abundant albatross along the eastern Pacific Coast and occurs off California in all months of the year (Briggs et al. 1987). This albatross also breeds in the Hawaiian Archipelago; population numbers were estimated to be 200,000 individuals in the early 1990s (Whittow 1993a) although that number may be decreasing (Brooke 2004). After breeding in June, adults

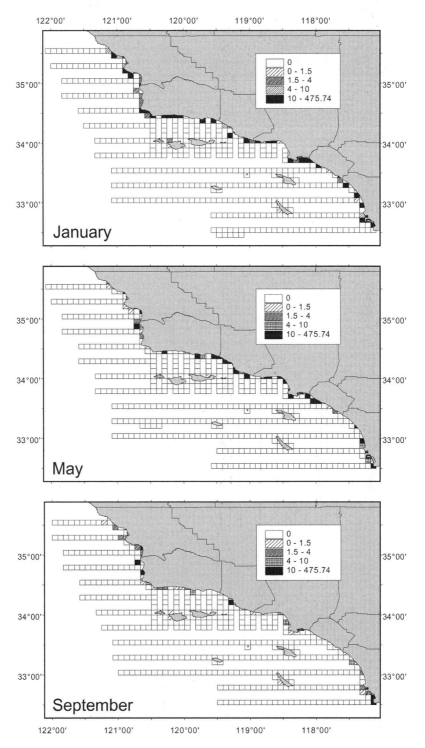

FIGURE 10. Western Grebe densities (birds/km²) and distribution off southern California from 1999–2002 during January, May, and September.

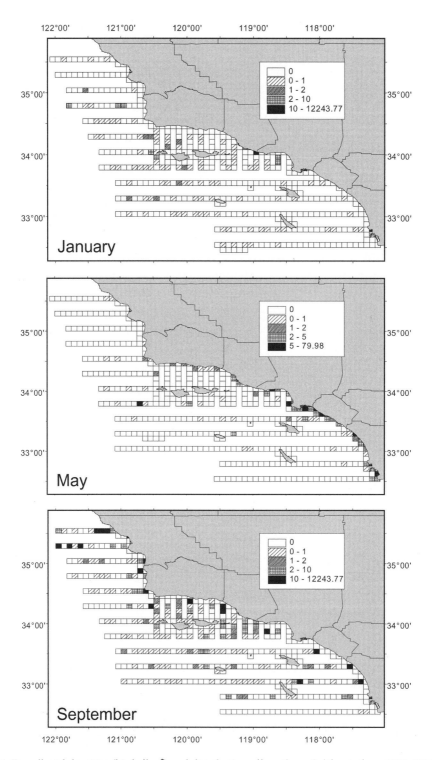

FIGURE 11. Procellariid densities (birds/km²) and distribution off southern California from 1999–2002 during January, May, and September.

disperse into the north Pacific Ocean and are most abundant off California from June through August (Stallcup 1990, Whittow 1993a). Briggs et al. (1987) observed maximum numbers of birds off southern California in May or June and within 25 km of the Santa Rosa-Cortes Ridge, especially near San Miguel Island and Tanner and Cortez banks. In 1999–2002, we observed only eight Black-footed Albatrosses with most in May 2000 northwest of the SCB (Fig. 12). On average, sightings occurred <45 km from land (four sightings <20 km from land) and over deep waters (1,260 m; Fig. 12). Low numbers of sightings in both 1975–1978 and 1999–2002 prevented trend analysis.

Laysan Albatross (Phoebastria immutabilis)

Laysan Albatrosses are the most abundant albatrosses in the Northern Hemisphere with an estimated global population of 2,500,000 individuals in the early 1990s (Whittow 1993b). They breed almost entirely in the Hawaiian Archipelago from Kure Atoll to Kauai. In the 1980s, a small breeding colony was discovered on Guadalupe Island off central Baja California, Mexico, and other incipient colonies have developed in the Revillagigedos Islands and Alijos Rock, Mexico (Whittow 1993b). In southern California, Laysan Albatrosses occurred primarily in deeper water and far offshore (Stallcup 1990). In 1975–1978, Briggs et al. (1987) observed only seven birds, most of which were recorded over deep water and seaward of the continental shelf. In 1999–2002, we observed only six birds (Fig. 13); these sightings occurred in January in all years and in May 2001 over waters with an average depth of 1,855 m and 72 km from shore. Two Laysan Albatrosses were recorded together in January 2001 and, in May 2001, a third individual was observed on the same transect line (<2 km away). The few sightings in both 1975–1978 and 1999–2002 prevented examining differences among survey periods.

Northern Fulmar (Fulmarus glacialis)

Northern Fulmars breed at several Alaskan colonies and in the winter are distributed widely across the Pacific Ocean south to Baja California, and Sonora, Mexico (Hatch and Nettleship 1998). Briggs et al. (1987) observed Northern Fulmars off California in all seasons with maximum abundances occurring off southern California in December–January and then again in March, indicating passage south to Mexican waters in winter and return north through the SCB in spring. Northern Fulmars

occurred in greatest densities 5–40 km from shore but also were observed 460 km offshore (maximum offshore distance surveyed; Briggs et al. 1987). We observed Northern Fulmars in all survey months and distributed throughout the study area in January (Fig. 14).

In 1999–2002, at-sea densities of Northern Fulmars differed among seasons and sub-areas with greatest densities in January and in S2 (Table 1b). Only four Northern Fulmars were observed on coastal transects, one near Point Mugu (CMC) and three near San Miguel Island. At sea densities in 1975–1983 were greater than densities in 1999–2002 for the entire study area, S3, and S4; were lower in S5; and did not differ significantly in S1 and S2 (Tables 7a, 7b).

Sooty Shearwater and Short-tailed Shearwater

Sooty and Short-tailed shearwaters were difficult to distinguish from the air, so we consider them together here although the vast majority of these birds are assumed to be Sooty Shearwaters. Both shearwaters breed in New Zealand, Chile, and Australia from October–May and migrate to the northern Pacific Ocean from May–September (Everett and Pitman 1993, Warham 1996). Short-tailed Shearwaters are uncommon off California in fall and winter, whereas Sooty Shearwaters are often very abundant. In the 1970s, millions of Sooty Shearwaters were estimated off California (Briggs and Chu 1986). From 1987–1994, Sooty Shearwater numbers decreased by 80–90% coincident with increased sea-surface temperatures throughout the CCS (Veit et al. 1997). Spear and Ainley (1999) suggested that changes in migratory movements may partly explain reduced southern California numbers. From 1975–1983, maximum numbers off southern California occurred in May in the shelf waters off Point Conception (Briggs et al. 1987). In 1999–2002, Sooty and Short-tailed shearwaters were distributed throughout the study area in May with largest concentrations near the northern Channel Islands (Fig. 15).

At-sea densities of Sooty and Short-tailed shearwaters differed among seasons and sub-areas (Table 5). Densities at sea were greatest in May when shearwaters occurred on all at-sea transect lines (Tables 1a–e; Fig. 15). Greatest densities occurred in S3 in May and in S1 in September (Tables 1a, 1c). Densities on coastal transects did not differ among seasons or the four sub-areas in which they occurred (CMC, SMC, NIC, and SIC; Table 6). A single flock of 6,000 Sooty and Short-tailed shearwaters near Point Sal accounted for 40% of shearwaters observed.

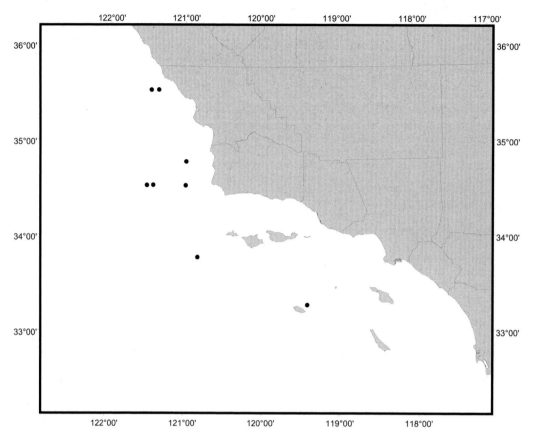

FIGURE 12. Black-footed Albatross sightings off southern California during January and May of 2000 and January and September of 2001.

At-sea densities of Sooty and Short-tailed shearwaters were greater in 1975–1983 than in 1999–2002 in S2, S4, and S5; were lower in S3; and did not differ significantly for the entire study area or S1 (Tables 7a, 7b). These results agree with declining populations reported throughout the range of the Sooty Shearwater, supporting the contention that declines may be an indication of global changes (Veit et al. 1997, Lyver et al. 1999). In addition, our greater sampling effort may have resulted in better estimates of these patchily distributed shearwaters compared with previous surveys; thus, the population decline that we estimated may be conservative.

Pink-footed Shearwater

Pink-footed Shearwaters breed off Chile from November–May and are listed as a threatened species due to a restricted breeding range and population declines (Guicking et al. 2001). About 20,000 breeding pairs nest at their main

breeding colony at Mocha Island (Guicking et al. 2001). Briggs et al. (1987) observed Pink-footed Shearwaters in the SCB in almost every month. Greatest densities occurred in May or June and decreased until a second maximum in August to September. In 1975–1978 in the SCB, shearwaters were common near the Santa Rosa-Cortes Ridge in the Santa Barbara Channel and the southern coasts of the northern Channel Islands (Briggs et al. 1987). In 1999–2002, we observed Pink-footed Shearwaters throughout the study area in September, primarily south of Point Conception in May, and near Point Conception in January (Fig. 16).

At-sea densities of Pink-footed Shearwaters differed among seasons but did not differ significantly among sub-areas (Table 5). Densities were greatest in September and lowest in January (Tables 1a–e). Coastal densities did not differ between NMC and NIC but greater densities occurred in September than in May (Table 6). At-sea densities of Pink-footed Shearwaters were greater in 1975–1983 than in 1999–2002 in

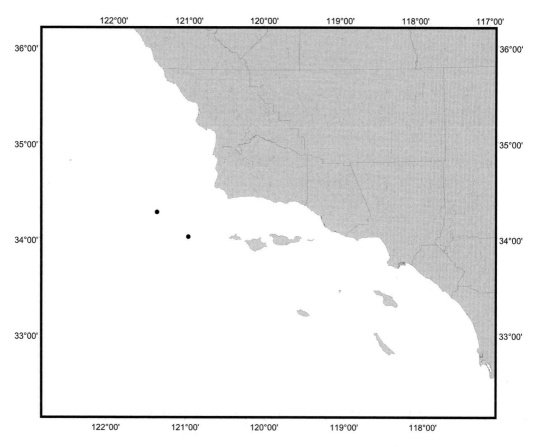

FIGURE 13. Laysan Albatross sightings off southern California during January of 2000 and 2001.

S2 and S5; lower in S4; but did not differ significantly for the entire study area, S1, and S3 (Tables 7a, 7b).

Black-vented Shearwater (Puffinus opisthomelas)

Black-vented Shearwaters breed off the west coast of Baja California, Mexico, with >95% on Natividad Island (Keitt et al. 2000). Black-vented Shearwaters are listed as a Species of Special Concern by the International Union for the Conservation of Nature (Birdlife International 2003). Post-breeding birds disperse northward in July or August and are most abundant off southern California in November, December, and January usually <25 km from shore (Everett 1988, Keitt et al. 2000). Briggs et al. (1987) recorded Black-vented Shearwaters in all months except April with maximum numbers from September–December. Ainley (1976) noted that Black-vented Shearwaters occurred farther northward during years of warm water associated with El Niño events. In September 1977 (an El Niño year), Black-

vented Shearwaters occurred throughout the SCB east of the Santa Rosa-Cortes Ridge, in the eastern Santa Barbara Channel, and near Oceanside (Briggs et al. 1987). In 1975–1978, shearwaters were recorded in near-shore waters from south of Dana Point to San Diego (Briggs et al. 1987). In 1999–2002, we primarily observed Black-vented Shearwaters in the eastern Santa Barbara Channel generally <10 km from shore (Fig. 17).

At-sea densities differed among seasons and the four sub-areas where they were observed (S1, S3, S4, and S5; Table 5). In 1999–2002, densities were three times greater in January than in September (Tables 1a–e). Seventy-seven percent of Black-vented Shearwaters recorded at sea occurred in S3. We observed one Black-vented Shearwater in May and one in September 1999. On coastal transects, we observed only two birds between Anacapa and Santa Cruz islands in September 2001. We were not able to obtain Black-vented Shearwater data for the period 1975–1983 and could not compare studies statistically.

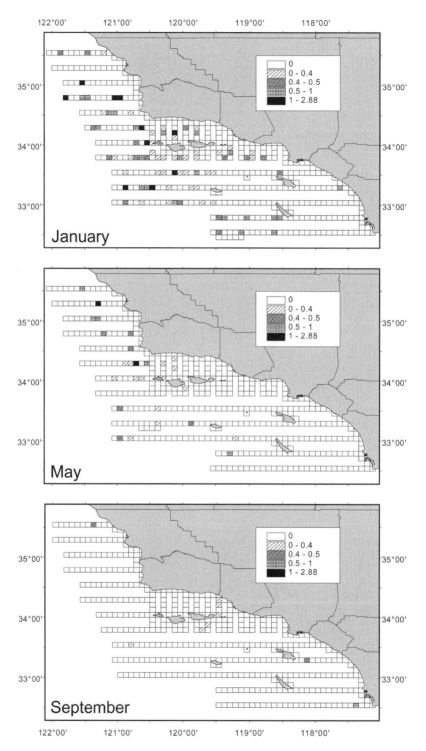

FIGURE 14. Northern Fulmar densities (birds/km²) and distribution off southern California from 1999–2002 during January, May, and September.

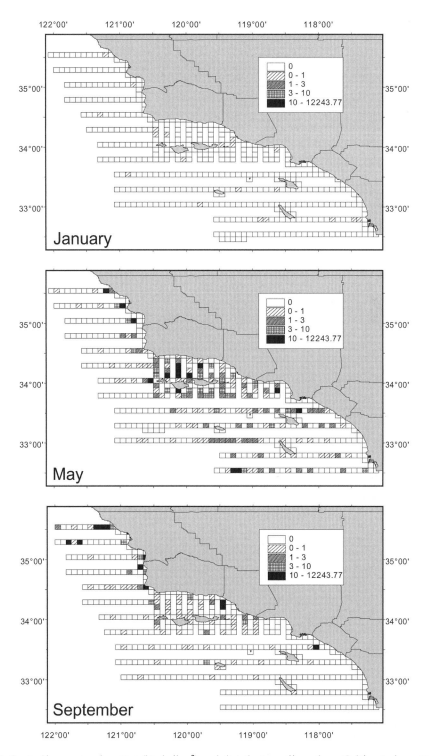

FIGURE 15. Sooty Shearwater densities (birds/km²) and distribution off southern California from 1999–2002 during January, May, and September.

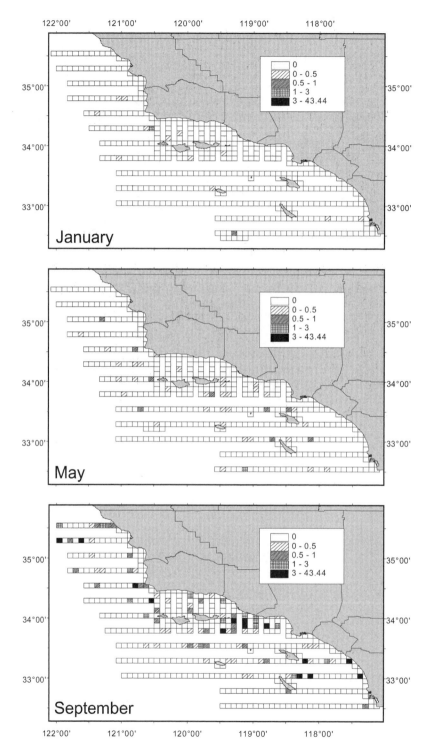

FIGURE 16. Pink-footed Shearwater densities (birds/km²) and distribution off southern California from 1999–2002 during January, May, and September.

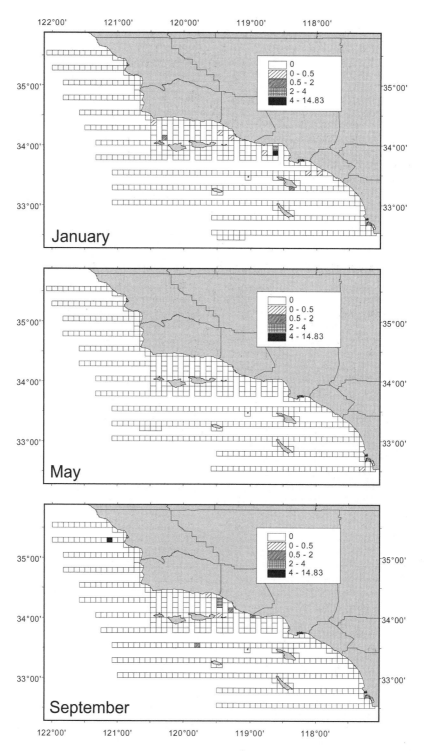

FIGURE 17. Black-vented Shearwater densities (birds/km²) and distribution off southern California from 1999–2002 during January, May, and September.

Leach's Storm-Petrel (Oceanodroma leucorhoa)

Leach's Storm-Petrels are the most widespread procellariiform breeding in the Northern Hemisphere and, in the eastern Pacific, breed from the Aleutian Islands, Alaska, to Guadalupe Island, Baja California, Mexico (Huntington et al. 1996). In the SCB, Leach's Storm-Petrels breed on Prince, Sutil, Santa Barbara, and Coronado islands (H. Carter, unpubl. data). Although difficult to census, 314 breeding birds were estimated for the SCB in 1991 (H. Carter, unpubl. data). Briggs et al. (1987) observed Leach's Storm-Petrels in all months of the year with greatest densities off southern California from June through October and lower densities from December through May. In spring 1975–1978, Leach's Storm-Petrels occurred from San Miguel Island to Cortez Bank and eastward to just south of San Clemente Island (Briggs et al. 1987). In late summer, distribution shifted northwestward, seaward of San Nicolas and San Miguel islands (Briggs et al. 1987). In 1999–2002, we found a similar distribution as in 1975–1978 but did not find birds as close to shore in May and found a more northward distribution in September (Fig. 18). For all surveys combined, we observed 64% of birds in the southwest portion of the SCB between 33° and 34° latitude and 120° and 121° longitude and, in January, they occurred only within this area.

At-sea densities of Leach's Storm-Petrels differed among seasons and sub-areas (Table 5). Greatest densities occurred in May and September and very few birds occurred in January (Tables 1a–e). Greatest densities were in S5 and lowest densities in S4. Leach's Storm-Petrels were observed in all sub-areas in all months except for January when they were observed only in S5 (Tables 1a–e). We did not observe Leach's Storm-Petrels on coastal transects. At-sea densities of Leach's Storm-Petrels in 1975–1983 were greater than densities in 1999–2002 for the entire study area, S1, S2, S3, and S4; but lower in S5 (Tables 7a, 7b).

Black Storm-Petrel (Oceanodroma melania)

Black Storm-Petrels breed primarily in the Gulf of California, Mexico, although smaller numbers also breed along the west coast of Baja California, Mexico, and southern California (Pitman and Speich 1976, Sowls et al. 1980, Everett and Anderson 1991). In the SCB, storm-petrels breed on Santa Barbara, Sutil, and Coronado islands, and possibly on Prince (<1 km north of San Miguel Island) and San Clemente islands (H. Carter, unpubl. data). Breeding numbers are difficult to estimate because Black Storm-Petrels nest in inaccessible burrows or crevices and are active at breeding colonies only at night. In 1991, 274 breeding birds were estimated at Santa Barbara and Sutil islands representing >54% increase from 1975–1978 (H. Carter, unpubl. data).

Briggs et al. (1987) observed Black Storm-Petrels in all months with maximum abundances in August and September. In 1975–1978, birds occurred primarily south of Point Conception and <50 km from the mainland, although aggregations of birds also were observed at Forty Mile Bank (30 km southeast of San Clemente Island), near Santa Barbara Island, and along the Santa Rosa-Cortes Ridge (Briggs et al. 1987). In 1999–2001 in September and May, Black Storm-Petrels occurred between Cortez Bank and San Diego, <40 km from the northern Channel Islands, and 50–100 km from Point Buchon in September (Fig. 19).

At-sea densities of Black Storm-Petrels differed among seasons and sub-areas (Table 5). Birds were observed in nearly equal abundance in May and September, but were virtually absent in January (Tables 1a–e). Densities were greatest in S4 and S5 (Tables 1d, 1e). Black Storm-Petrels were not observed on any coastal transect. At-sea densities in 1999–2002 were greater than in 1975–1983 for the entire study area, S3, S4, and S5; but lower in S1 and S2 (Tables 7a, 7b).

Ashy Storm-Petrel (Oceanodroma homochroa)

An estimated 10,000 Ashy Storm-Petrels occur mainly off California, with small numbers off Baja California, Mexico (Ainley 1995; Carter et al., in press). Ashy Storm-Petrels occur year-round in waters of the continental slope and slightly farther to sea and do not disperse far from breeding locations (Ainley 1995). In the SCB, breeding occurs on the Coronado and Todos Santos islands, Baja California, Mexico, and six California Channel Islands (i.e., not Santa Rosa and San Nicolas), and small numbers may breed at Vandenberg Air Force Base (Carter et al., in press). The state of California designated the Ashy Storm-Petrel as a Species of Special Concern (J. Remsen, unpubl. data) and the USDI Fish and Wildlife Service designated it as a bird of conservation concern (USDI Fish and Wildlife Service 2002). In 1991, H. Carter (unpubl. data) estimated 3,135 birds in the SCB but differences in survey protocols and efforts from past studies made trends in population size impossible to assess. However, decline has been noted at the South Farallon Islands in central California (W. Sydeman, unpubl. data). Surveys in 1994–1996 found more widespread breeding in the Channel Islands and higher

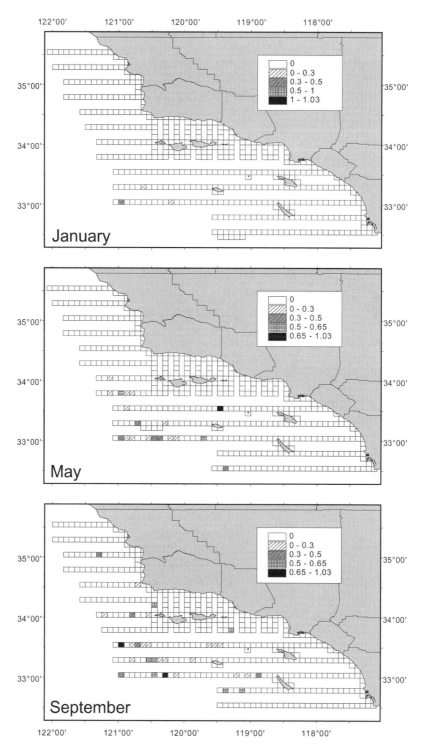

FIGURE 18. Leach's Storm-Petrel densities (birds/km²) and distribution off southern California from 1999–2002 during January, May, and September.

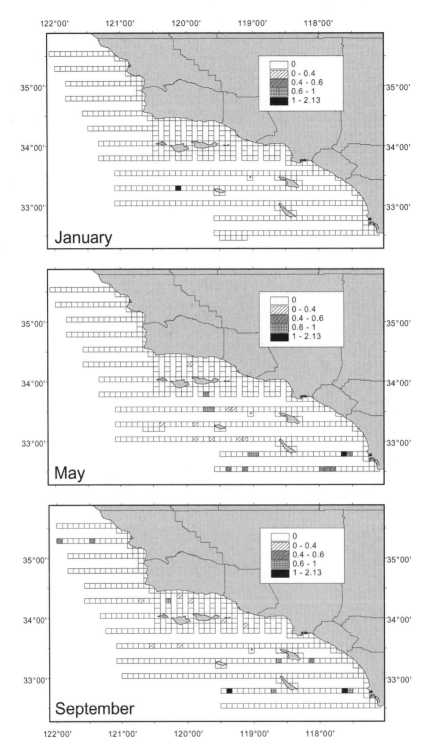

FIGURE 19. Black Storm-Petrel densities (birds/km²) and distribution off southern California from 1999–2002 during January, May, and September.

breeding population estimates (Carter et al., in press). From 1995–2003, numbers breeding at study areas on Santa Cruz Island did not change to a great degree (McIver 2002; Carter et al., in press). Off southern California, Briggs et al. (1987) observed Ashy Storm-Petrels in greatest abundance near San Miguel Island from April–June. After October, birds occurred near San Clemente and Santa Catalina islands, over the Santa Rosa-Cortes Ridge, and in the western Santa Barbara Channel to Point Buchon (Briggs et al. 1987). In 1999–2002, we observed Ashy Storm-Petrels throughout the study area with aggregations between Santa Cruz and San Nicolas islands, in the western Santa Barbara Channel, and 10–70 km offshore from San Miguel Island to Point Buchon (Fig. 20).

In 1999–2002, at-sea densities differed among seasons and sub-areas (Table 5). Densities were greatest in May and September, and we observed birds in all sub-areas and in all months except during January in S2 and S3 (Tables 1a–e). We did not observe Ashy Storm-Petrels on coastal transects. At-sea densities of Ashy Storm-Petrels in 1999–2002 were greater than densities in 1975–1983 for the entire study area, S1, S2, S3, and S5 (Table 7). We did not test statistical differences in S5 because Briggs et al. (1987) did not observe birds in S5. However, lower densities in 1999–2002 may reflect undocumented declines at some SCB colonies, decline at the South Farallon Islands, or variation in foraging and wintering areas between years.

Brown Pelican (Pelecanus occidentalis)

The Brown Pelican subspecies, *P. o. californicus,* currently breeds from the California Channel islands south along the Pacific coast of Baja, California, Mexico, throughout the Gulf of California, and south along the Pacific coast of Mexico to Isla Tres Marias and ranges from southern British Columbia, Canada, to Colimas, Mexico (Shields 2002). Greatest pelican abundance in southern California occurs in late summer and early fall coincident with dispersal of birds from breeding colonies in Mexico; abundance is lowest after breeding adults return to breeding colonies in Mexico in early winter (Anderson and Anderson 1976; Briggs et al. 1981, 1983; Jaques 1994; Jaques et al. 1996). In the 1960s and 1970s, Brown Pelicans experienced extremely poor breeding success in southern California due to eggshell thinning caused by DDE contamination (Keith et al. 1971, Risebrough 1972, Jehl 1973, Anderson et al. 1975, Anderson and Gress 1983, Gress and Anderson 1983). Reproductive success did not rebound until the late 1970s (F. Gress, unpubl.

data). In 1969–1978, <800 nests were estimated to be on West Anacapa Island. In 1991, about 5,300 pairs were estimated on West Anacapa Island and about 600 breeding pairs were estimated on Santa Barbara Island (H. Carter, unpubl. data).

Briggs et al. (1987) reported lowest densities of Brown Pelicans in California from December through March and greatest densities in September and October with most birds <20 km from shore. Similarly, in 1999–2002 we observed greatest densities in September with 83% observed on at-sea transects <10 km from shore. Brown Pelicans typically roost on land when not feeding at all times of year, leading to relatively low densities at sea, compared to some other seabirds.

In 1999–2002, Brown Pelicans were distributed along coastlines and near roosting sites throughout the study area and occurred in all at-sea sub-areas (Fig. 21). They generally were more abundant along mainland than island coastlines and densities were greatest along the CMC in May (possibly due to breeding activities on Anacapa Island) and NMC and SMC in September (Tables 2–4). In all survey months, Brown Pelicans were most abundant near Point Loma, Palos Verdes, Point Sal, and along the mainland coast of the Santa Barbara Channel and the southern coast of Santa Rosa Island (Fig. 21).

At-sea densities of Brown Pelicans differed significantly among seasons and sub-areas (Table 5) and were greatest in September when breeding birds from Mexico arrived in the SCB. Densities were generally greatest in S3, probably due to the proximity of numerous available roost sites on the northern Channel Islands and on the central mainland coast (Point Conception to Point Dume; Table 1c). We observed only 12 Brown Pelicans in S2. Along coastlines, their densities were greatest in September (Tables 2–4, 6). Densities did not differ significantly among coastal sub-areas (Table 6).

For the entire study area, at-sea densities of Brown Pelicans were greater in 1999–2002 than in 1975–1983 (Tables 7a, 7b), reflecting increased breeding populations in the Gulf of California and in southern California. Pelican densities were lower in S4 and S5; higher in S2 where no pelicans were observed in 1975–1983; and did not differ significantly in S1 and S3 (Tables 7a, 7b).

CORMORANTS

Densities of all cormorants, including those not identified to species, were combined (Fig. 22) because the three species, Brandt's, Pelagic,

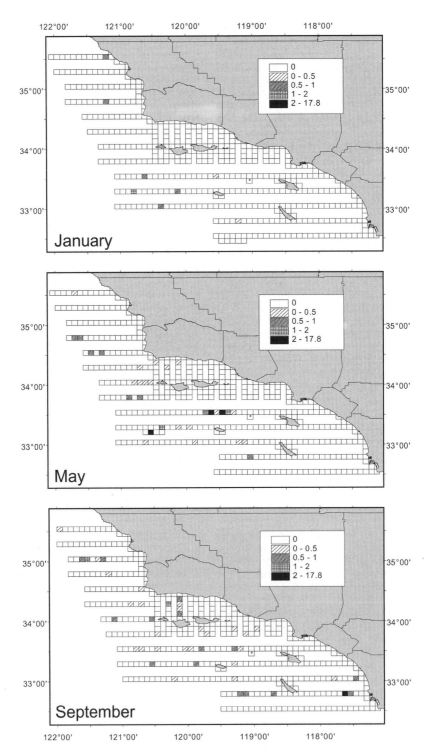

FIGURE 20. Ashy Storm-Petrel densities (birds/km^2) and distribution off southern California from 1999–2002 during January, May, and September.

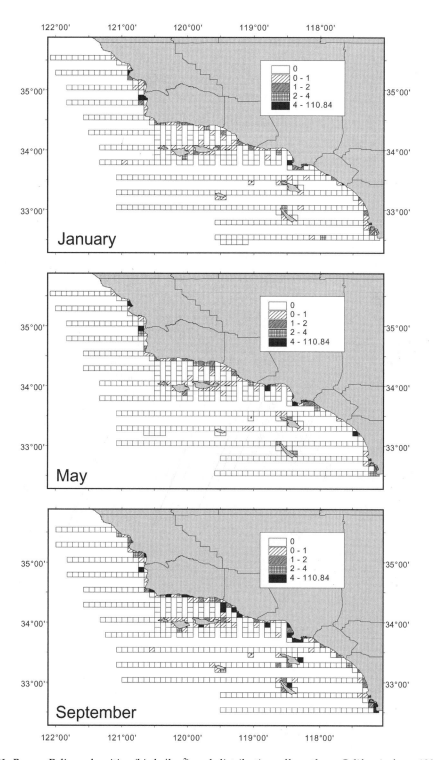

FIGURE 21. Brown Pelican densities (birds/km²) and distribution off southern California from 1999–2002 during January, May, and September.

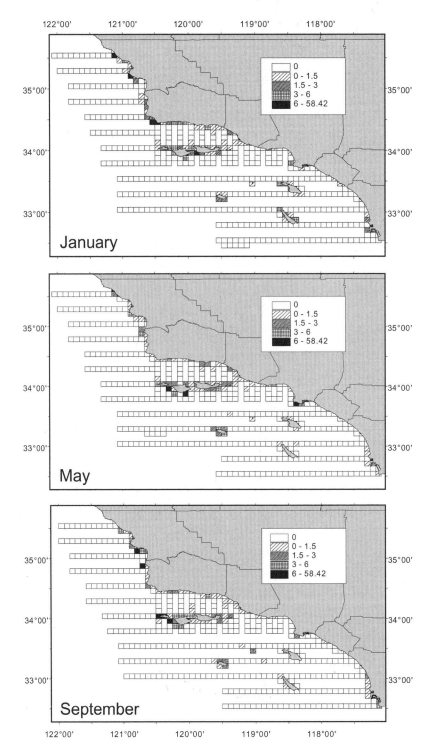

FIGURE 22. Cormorant densities (birds/km²) and distribution off southern California from 1999–2002 during January, May, and September.

and Double-crested cormorants (*Phalacrocorax penicillatus*, *P. pelagicus*, and *P. auritus*) were difficult to distinguish from the air and 45% of observed cormorants were unidentified (Fig. 23). Cormorants occurred in every at-sea sub-area except S2 and in every season (Fig. 22). At all times of year, cormorants typically roost on land when they are not feeding, and thus have relatively low densities at sea compared with other seabird families. At-sea densities of cormorants did not differ among seasons, but did differ among sub-areas, with greatest densities occurring in S3 (Tables 1, 5). Coastal densities of cormorants did not differ among seasons, but did differ among sub-areas with greatest densities along the NMC in all months (Tables 2–4, 6). At-sea densities were greater in 1999–2002 than in 1975–1983 for the entire study area, S1, and S5; and were lower in S3 and S4 (Tables 7a, 7b).

Double-crested Cormorant

Double-crested Cormorants are the most numerous and widely distributed of the six North American cormorants but are rarely observed far from land (Hatch and Weseloh 1999). Along the Pacific Coast, the subspecies *P. a. albociliatus* breeds from southern British Columbia, Canada, to the Gulf of California in marine and estuarine habitats (Harrison 1983, Carter et al. 1995). In the SCB Double-crested Cormorants experienced reduced breeding success in the mid-twentieth century due to DDE contamination (Gress et al. 1973; F. Gress, unpubl. data). In 1969, severe eggshell thinning from DDE contamination was discovered in colonies on West Anacapa Island and South Coronado Island, Mexico (Gress et al. 1973, Jehl 1973). Reduced breeding success continued until the early 1970s at the West Anacapa Island colony, but thereafter, breeding success gradually improved (Anderson and Gress 1983; F. Gress, unpubl. data). In 1991, the estimated 5,000 breeding pairs in southern California represented greater than a four-fold increase over 1975–1978 estimates (H. Carter, unpubl. data).

In the SCB, breeding colonies are located on Prince, West Anacapa, and Santa Barbara islands (H. Carter, unpubl. data). Only a few Double-crested Cormorants were observed at sea in 1975–1983 and these were <3 km from breeding colonies (Briggs et al. 1987). In 1999–2002, Double-crested Cormorants were observed consistently near Point Loma and Palos Verdes, south of Point Buchon, north of Morro Bay, along the mainland coast of the Santa Barbara Channel, and near the four northern Channel Islands, and San Nicolas

Island (Fig. 24). We observed 86% of Double-crested Cormorants <1 km from shore. In May and September, individuals were occasionally observed 20–30 km northwest of Santa Barbara Island.

We found that at-sea densities of Double-crested Cormorants differed among seasons and the four at-sea sub-areas in which they occurred (S1, S3, S4, and S5; Table 5). At-sea densities were generally greatest in January and in S1 (Table 1a). In May and September, densities were greatest in S3 near breeding colonies (Table 1c). Densities differed among coastal sub-areas, but greatest densities occurred in the CMC in each survey month (Tables 2–4, 6). Double-crested Cormorants occurred in all coastal sub-areas, and coastal densities were up to 40-fold greater than at-sea densities.

Statistical comparisons between 1975–1983 and 1999–2002 surveys were limited to the entire study area, S3, and S4 because of limited observations in other sub-areas during 1975–1983. At-sea densities of Double-crested Cormorants were greater in 1999–2002 than in 1975–1978 for the entire study area and in S3, but were lower in S4 (Tables 7a, 7b). Greater densities were consistent with increased SCB breeding populations. Although continent-wide increases also may have led to increased wintering birds coming from other areas, we could not determine if other breeding populations were represented in the winter.

Brandt's Cormorant

Brandt's Cormorants nest along the Pacific Coast from southwest Vancouver Island, British Columbia, Canada, to southern Baja California, Mexico, including portions of the Gulf of California (Wallace and Wallace 1998). They are one of the most widely distributed and abundant breeding seabirds in southern California and currently breed on all Channel Islands except Santa Catalina Island (H. Carter, unpubl. data). The population size of Brandt's Cormorants decreased in the 1950s and 1960s likely because of breeding failures caused by DDE contamination and human disturbance (McChesney et al. 1997; G. Hunt, unpubl. data). At Santa Barbara and San Nicolas islands, cormorant abundance decreased by 50–90% from the 1950s–1977 (McChesney et al. 1997; G. Hunt, unpubl. data). In 1991, however, about 14,700 breeding pairs were estimated in southern California, a four-fold increase since 1975–1978 (7,600 birds; H. Carter, unpubl. data). In 1975–1983, Brandt's Cormorants occurred primarily in shallow waters <10 km from shore and <25 km from island or mainland roosts or colonies

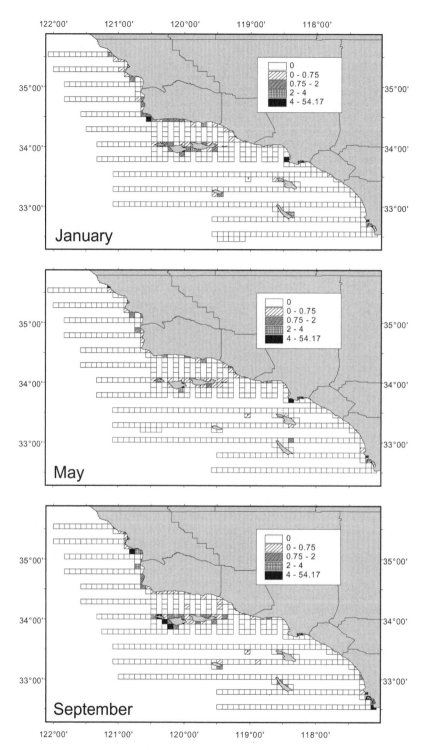

FIGURE 23. Unidentified cormorant densities (birds/km²) and distribution off southern California from 1999–2002 during January, May, and September.

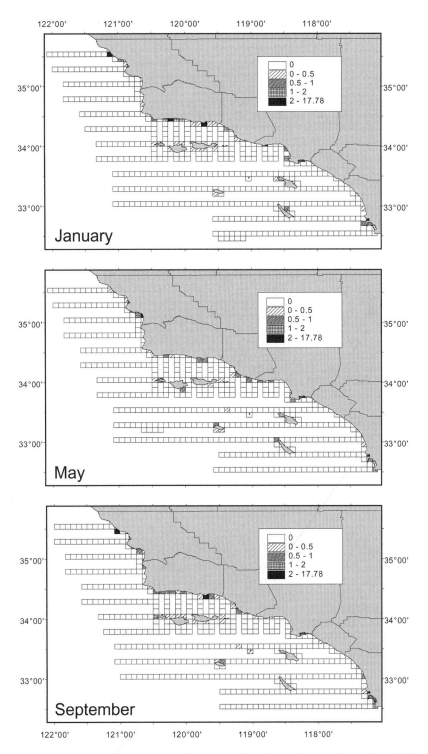

FIGURE 24. Double-crested Cormorant densities (birds/km²) and distribution off southern California from 1999–2002 during January, May, and September.

(Briggs et al. 1987). Along mainland coasts, birds consistently occurred near large roosts and near Point Loma, Palos Verdes, Point Sal, and Point Buchon (Fig. 11). Brandt's Cormorants were present at Santa Catalina Island in January and San Clemente Island in January and September. In May, however, reduced densities occurred in the southeastern SCB and increased densities occurred in the northern SCB where most breeding colonies were located.

In 1999–2002, at-sea densities of Brandt's Cormorants did not differ significantly among seasons but did differ among the four sub-areas in which they occurred (S1, S3, S4, and S5; Table 5). We observed greatest densities in S3 and S5 (Tables 1c, 1e). In all seasons, Brandt's Cormorants were concentrated near the northern Channel Islands and near San Nicolas Island (Fig. 25). This distribution corresponds to the presence of large breeding colonies and roost sites on these islands. Coastal densities of Brandt's Cormorants did not differ significantly among seasons, but did differ among sub-areas with greatest densities occurring along Channel Island coastlines, especially along the NIC (Tables 2–4, 6). We observed greater densities of Brandt's Cormorants at sea in 1999–2002 than in 1975–1983 for the entire study area and in each of the four sub-areas in which they occurred (S1, S3, S4, and S5; Tables 7a, 7b), reflecting increased SCB breeding populations between survey periods.

Pelagic Cormorant (Phalacrocorax pelagicus)

Pelagic Cormorants are the most coastal of the southern California cormorants and are rarely observed more than a few kilometers from shore (Sowls et al. 1980, Ainley et al. 1990). Pelagic Cormorants breed from Alaska to the Coronado Islands in northern Baja California, Mexico (Wilbur 1987, Howell and Webb 1995), and occur south to central Baja California, Mexico (Hobson 1997). They breed on five Channel Islands. In 1991, H. Carter (unpubl. data) estimated about 1,400 breeding pairs in the SCB, a three-fold increase over 1975–1978 estimates.

Briggs et al. (1987) observed few Pelagic Cormorants, most north of Point Conception and <10 km from shore. Similarly, we observed most birds <10 km from shore, but unlike the previous study, >80% of the birds occurred south of Point Conception near breeding colonies at San Miguel, Santa Rosa, and Santa Cruz islands. Along the mainland coastline, we consistently observed birds near Point Buchon and Morro Bay in May and September (Fig. 26). Although Pelagic Cormorants breed at Santa Barbara Island (H. Carter, unpubl. data), we did not observe birds near that island in May 1999–2001. The few birds observed in September surveys, however, occurred within 10 km of Santa Barbara Island.

We observed only nine Pelagic Cormorants on at-sea transects and did not have sufficient data to compare at-sea densities among season, sub-area, or to 1975–1983. Most of our sightings occurred in the Santa Barbara Channel, but two birds were seen near Morro Bay.

Along coastlines, densities of Pelagic Cormorants differed among seasons and sub-areas (Table 6). Greatest densities of birds occurred along the CMC and along the NIC (Tables 2–4). Coastal densities were similar in January and May, and few birds were observed in September surveys (Tables 2–4), suggesting little movement of wintering birds from more northern areas into southern California. Pelagic Cormorants were more easily identified to species in May, due to the presence of their conspicuous white flank patches. In January and September surveys, we probably included more Pelagic Cormorants as unidentified cormorants; therefore, our population estimates and distribution maps are probably incomplete in these months.

Surf Scoter and White-winged Scoter

Surf and White-winged scoters can be difficult to distinguish from the air. We identified only three White-winged Scoters in our surveys. Briggs et al. (1987) noted that White-winged Scoters accounted for 5–10% of all scoters observed south of the northern Channel Islands. Therefore, we combined both species for analyses and hereafter refer to them as Surf Scoters. Surf Scoters breed from the western Aleutian Islands, Alaska to British Columbia, Canada, and at several inland sites to eastern Canada (Savard et al. 1998). Scoters primarily winter from the eastern Aleutian Islands and southeast Alaska to central Baja California, Mexico, and the Gulf of California, Mexico (Savard et al. 1998). In 1975–1978, Surf Scoters arrived in the SCB in November and December with maximum abundances from December through March (Briggs et al. 1987). In winter 1975–1978, they most often occurred in near-shore waters in the eastern Santa Barbara Channel, along northern coasts of the northern Channel Islands, in Santa Monica Bay, and from south of Dana Point to San Diego (Briggs et al. 1987). In 1999–2002, Surf Scoters were recorded in all survey months and consistently observed near San Diego and Morro Bay and in the eastern Santa Barbara Channel (Fig. 27).

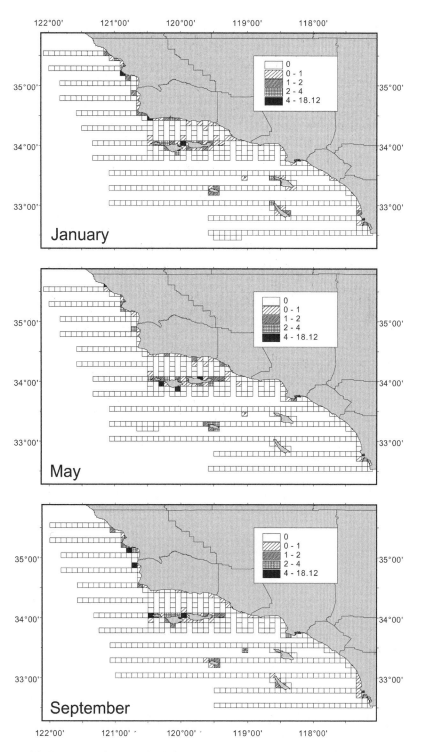

FIGURE 25. Brandt's Cormorant densities (birds/km2) and distribution off southern California from 1999–2002 during January, May, and September.

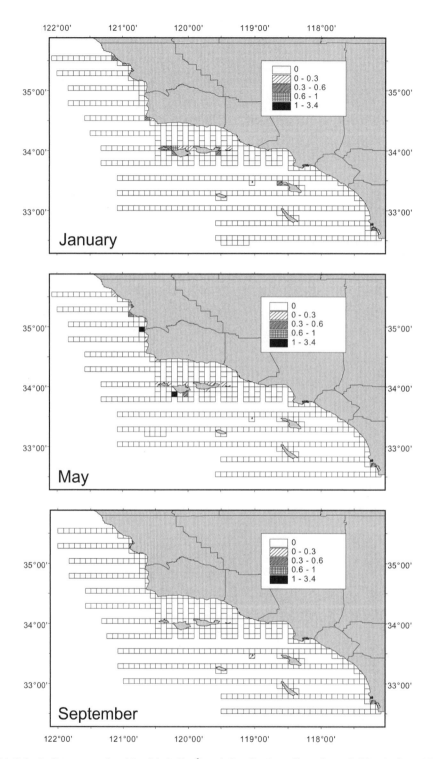

FIGURE 26. Pelagic Cormorant densities (birds/km²) and distribution off southern California from 1999–2002 during January, May, and September.

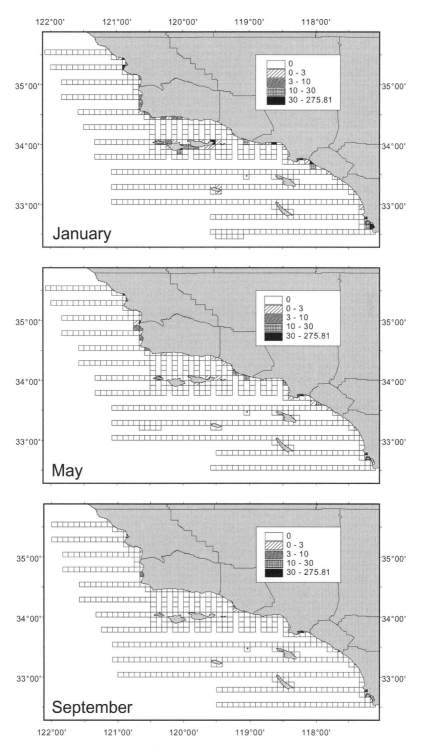

FIGURE 27. Surf Scoter densities (birds/km²) and distribution off southern California from 1999–2002 during January, May, and September.

We observed 126 Surf Scoters on at-sea transects in S1 and S3 in January and May and found no difference in densities between S1 and S3 or between January and May (Tables 1, 5). On coastal transects, densities differed among seasons and sub-areas (Table 6). Surf Scoters were most abundant in the SCB in January, least abundant in September, and were equally abundant in NMC and SMC (Tables 2–4).

Because we observed few Surf Scoters on at-sea transects, we did not compare them statistically with Briggs et al. (1987). Reduced numbers of White-winged Scoters has been reported along the Pacific Coast (D. Nysewander, unpubl. data), but we were unable to readily distinguish between Surf and White-winged scoters from the air, and thus could not assess differences in trends between species.

PHALAROPODINAE

We observed two species of phalaropes within the study area (Fig. 28). Red Phalaropes (*Phalaropus fulicaria*) and Red-necked Phalaropes (*P. lobatus*) were difficult to distinguish from the air. Consequently, 64% of all phalarope sightings were classified as unidentified phalaropes (Fig. 29). Briggs et al. (1987) found both phalarope species distributed throughout California waters from the shoreline to hundreds of kilometers offshore, but that only Red Phalaropes were likely to be observed >50 km from the coast. We also observed phalaropes throughout the SCB and that, when identifiable, Red Phalaropes were distributed farther from shore than Red-necked Phalaropes. Briggs et al. (1987) found spring migration (April–May) to be much more rapid than fall migration (July–October).

In 1992–2002, at-sea densities of phalaropes differed among seasons and sub-areas (Table 5). Greatest at-sea densities generally occurred in May and in S1 and S2 (Tables 1a, 1b). Few phalaropes occurred on coastal transects (Tables 2–4). At-sea densities were greater in 1975–1983 than in 1999–2002 for the entire study area, S3, S4, and S5, but did not differ significantly in S1 and S2 (Tables 7a, 7b). Given the rapid spring migration patterns and the timing of our surveys, we may not have captured periods of peak abundance.

Red-necked Phalarope

Red-necked Phalaropes winter at sea primarily off the coast of Peru and Chile (Rubega et al. 2000). Departure times for southward migration are protracted as Red-necked Phalaropes appear in the SCB from mid-June to late October and again when returning north from mid-April to early June (Lehman 1994).

In 1999–2002, at-sea densities of Red-necked Phalaropes differed among seasons but did not differ significantly among sub-areas (Table 5). Greatest densities occurred in May (Tables 1a–e). We only observed four Red-necked Phalaropes on coastal transects and all occurred on the north side of the northern Channel Islands. Red-necked Phalaropes were distributed throughout the study area in January, aggregated near Point Conception in May, and distributed throughout the western portion of the study area in September (Fig. 30). At-sea densities of Red-necked Phalaropes were greater in 1999–2002 than in 1975–1983 for the entire study area, S1 and S3 (Tables 7a, 7b). We did not compare densities in S2, S4, and S5 across decades because Briggs et al. (1987) did not observe phalaropes in these sub-areas.

Red Phalarope

Red Phalaropes are almost entirely pelagic outside the breeding season, but may occur on bays and coastal estuaries (Johnsgard 1981). Briggs et al. (1987) noted that northbound Red Phalaropes migrated through the SCB in April and May and southbound birds were present from August through November. In 1999–2002, Red Phalaropes were rare in January, scattered throughout the study area in May, and distributed north of the northern Channel Islands and Point Conception in September (Fig. 31).

At-sea densities of Red Phalaropes differed among seasons and sub-areas and were greatest in May and in S1 (Tables 1, 5). We did not observe Red Phalaropes on coastal transects. At-sea densities of Red Phalaropes were greater in 1999–2002 than in 1975–1983 for the entire study area, S1, S2, and S5; but were lower in S3 and S4 (Tables 7a, 7b).

LARIDAE

We observed 22 species of larids within the study area (Fig. 32). At-sea densities differed among seasons and sub-areas (Table 5). Greatest densities occurred in January and in S3 (Table 1c). Coastal densities were greatest in January primarily due to large numbers of wintering California Gulls (Tables 2–4, 6). At-sea densities of larids were greater in 1975–1983 than in 1999–2002 for the entire study area and in each sub-area except S2 where the difference was not significant (Tables 7a, 7b).

Heermann's Gull (Larus heermanni)

Heermann's Gulls nest almost entirely (>95% of the world breeding population of

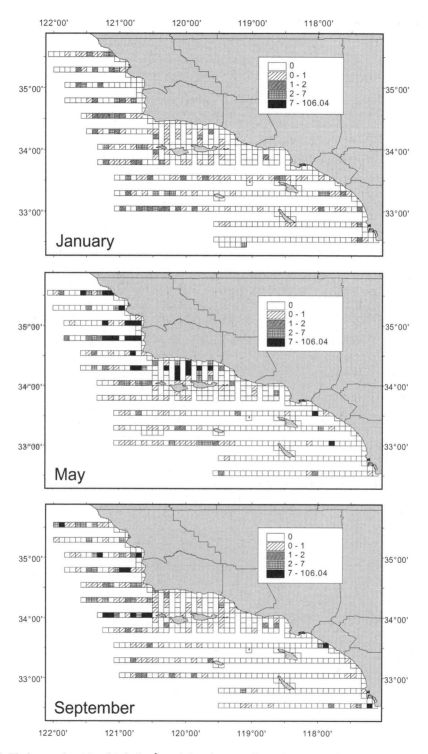

FIGURE 28. Phalarope densities (birds/km²) and distribution off southern California from 1999–2002 during January, May, and September.

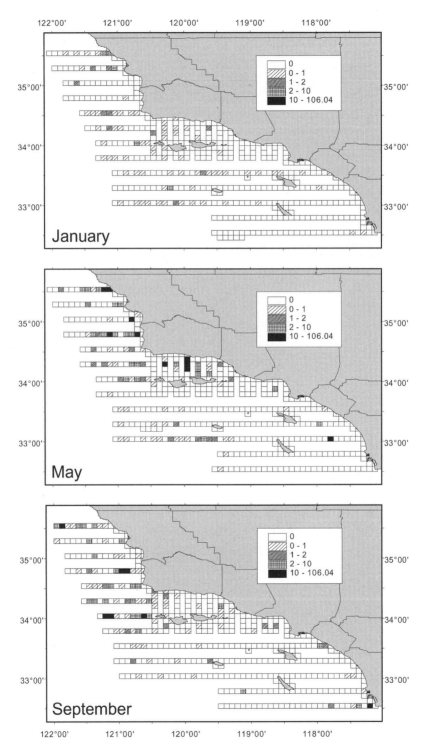

FIGURE 29. Unidentified phalarope densities (birds/km²) and distribution off southern California from 1999–2002 during January, May, and September.

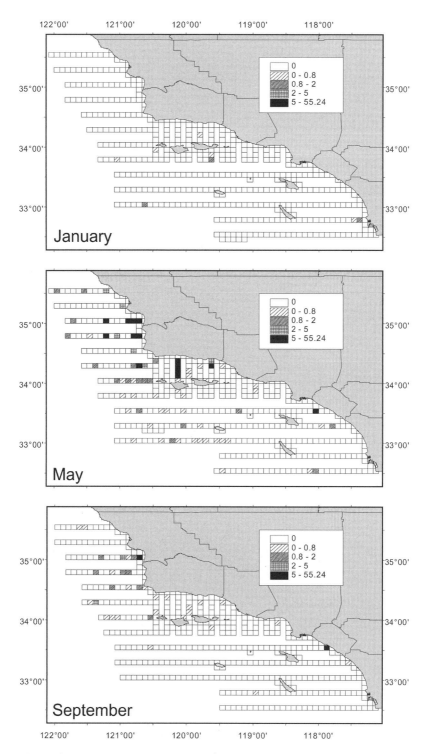

FIGURE 30. Red-necked Phalarope densities (birds/km²) and distribution off southern California from 1999–2002 during January, May, and September.

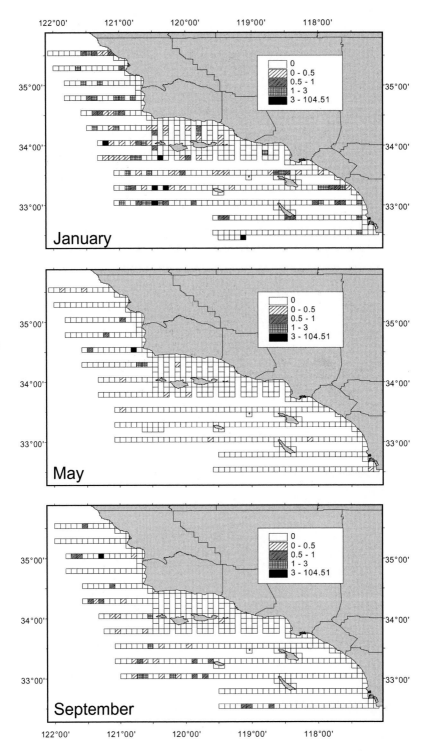

FIGURE 31. Red Phalarope densities (birds/km^2) and distribution off southern California from 1999–2002 during January, May, and September.

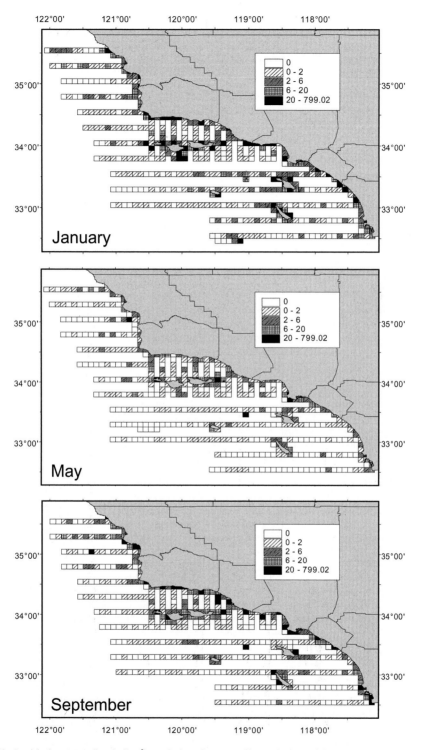

FIGURE 32. Larid densities (birds/km²) and distribution off southern California from 1999–2002 during January, May, and September.

130,000 breeding pairs) at Raza Island in the Gulf of California, Mexico (Velarde 1999). Small numbers also have bred on the west coast of Baja California, Mexico and along the U.S. mainland (Sowls et al. 1980, Everett and Anderson 1991). They disperse north to southern British Columbia in late summer and early fall (Campbell et al. 1990).

Briggs et al. (1987) reported post-breeding arrival of Heermann's Gulls off southern California from late April–June and departure to breeding areas in Mexico in early fall. In 1975–1978, they occurred consistently from Morro Bay to the Santa Barbara Channel and near San Diego (Briggs et al. 1987). In 1999–2002 during January and September, we consistently observed birds along the mainland coast from Point Sal to Gaviota, near Palos Verdes, Huntington Beach, and San Diego and along the coastlines of Santa Rosa, Santa Cruz, Anacapa, and San Clemente islands (Fig. 33). In May, we consistently observed Heermann's Gulls only near Palos Verdes. More than 86% of observed Heermann's Gulls occurred <1 km from shore.

In 1999–2002, at-sea densities of Heermann's Gulls did not differ significantly between the two seasons in which they were observed (January and September) but did differ among the four sub-areas in which they occurred (Table 5). At-sea densities were greatest in S3 and Heermann's Gulls were not observed in S2 (Tables 1b, 1c). Coastal densities differed among seasons, with greatest densities along the NMC in September and along the SCI in January (Tables 2–4, 6). At-sea densities in 1975–1983 were greater than densities in 1999–2002 for the entire study area, S1, S4, and S5; but were lower in S3 (Tables 7a, 7b). However we cannot confirm that this represents a decrease in population densities, since Heermann's Gulls occur in coastal areas and roost extensively on shore.

Bonaparte's Gull

Bonaparte's Gulls winter on the Pacific Coast, from southern British Columbia, Canada, to southern Baja California and Nayarit, Mexico (Burger and Gochfeld 2002). Off California, these gulls arrived in September–October and reached maximum numbers in late October–November (Briggs et al. 1987). Numbers declined through the winter and increased again in March–May. Although dispersed widely throughout shelf and slope waters, greatest numbers of birds occurred <40 km from shore (Briggs et al. 1987). In 1999–2002, Bonaparte's Gulls were observed only in January and May; >99% were seen south of Point Conception and >90% of birds occurred <40 km from shore (Fig. 34).

At-sea densities differed between the two seasons in which Bonaparte's Gulls were observed (January and May) and among sub-areas (Table 5). Greatest densities occurred in January and in S4 and S5 (Tables 1d, 1e). Coastal densities of Bonaparte's Gulls did not differ significantly between the two seasons (January and May) or the two sub-areas in which they were observed (CMC and SMCS: Table 6). At-sea densities in 1975–1983 were greater than in 1999–2002 for the entire study area and each of the five sub-areas (Tables 7a, 7b). Since coastal areas were not surveyed by Briggs et al. (1987), comparisons are limited. However, Bonaparte's Gulls do not roost on land as much as many other gulls, and we suspect that lower densities in 1999–2002 reflect a decrease in population numbers.

California Gull (Larus californicus)

California Gulls are one of the most common larids in California waters (Stallcup 1990). They breed at numerous sites on inland lakes from Mono Lake to San Francisco Bay, California, and from southern Colorado to Manitoba, Canada (Winkler 1996). Beginning in late summer, California Gulls winter on the eastern Pacific Coast from southern British Columbia, Canada, to southern Baja California, Mexico, and the Gulf of California (Winkler 1996). They undergo a northward migration in early fall to southern British Columbia coastal waters and move south by late fall reaching maximum abundances off central and southern California and Baja California, in January and February (Porter and Sealy 1981, Chilton and Sealy 1987, Winkler 1996). Breeding adults begin returning to inland colonies in February (Winkler 1996).

Briggs et al. (1987) found that California Gulls were the most abundant gulls in California near-shore waters in the fall and winter with California Gulls arriving in the SCB in late September or October. Shore-based surveys conducted from mainland and island coasts indicated maximum abundances in the SCB from January through March (Briggs et al. 1987). In 1999–2002, we observed California Gulls near mainland and island coastlines in all survey months and throughout southern California in January (Fig. 35). California Gulls were observed on all but two transect lines and 84% occurred <1 km from shore.

In 1999–2002, densities of California Gulls on at-sea transects differed among seasons and sub-areas (Table 5). Densities were greatest in January and lowest in September, indicating that most birds arrived after September

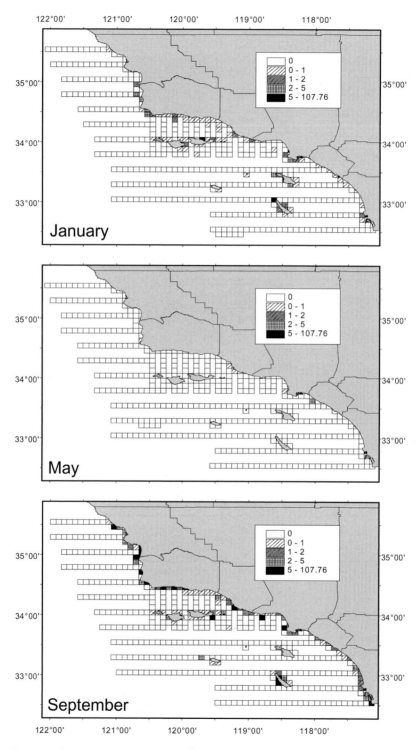

FIGURE 33. Heermann's Gull densities (birds/km²) and distribution off southern California from 1999–2002 during January, May, and September.

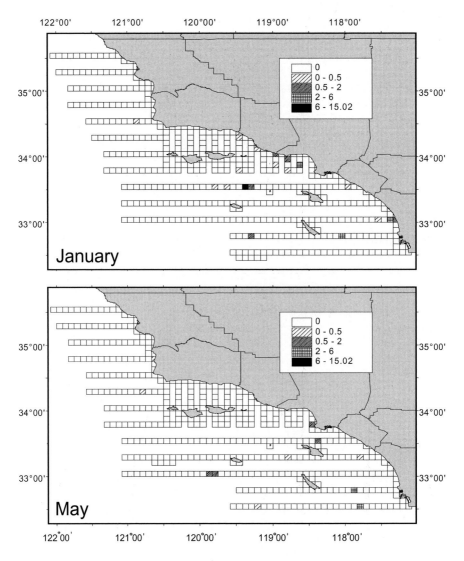

FIGURE 34. Bonaparte's Gull densities (birds/km^2) and distribution off southern California from 1999–2002 during January and May. No Bonaparte's Gulls were observed during September.

(Tables 1a–e). At-sea densities were greatest in S3 in January and September and in S1 and S4 in May (Tables 1a, 1c, 1d). On coastal transects, densities of California Gulls were greatest in January in all sub-areas (Tables 2–4, 6).

At-sea densities of California Gulls were greater in 1975–1983 than in 1999–2002 for the entire study area, S2, and S5; but did not differ significantly in S1, S3, and S4 (Tables 7a, 7b). However, since California Gulls mainly occur in coastal waters and roost extensively along shores, we could not compare densities in their most abundant areas so cannot confirm if this indicates a true decline in abundance or distribution shift.

Western Gull (Larus occidentalis)

Western Gulls breed from central Baja California, Mexico, to southwestern Washington (Speich and Wahl 1989, Penniman et al. 1990), and winter from the southern tip of Baja California, Mexico to Vancouver Island, Canada (Campbell et al. 1990, Howell and Webb 1995). The North American population was estimated at 40,000 pairs, making it a relatively rare *Larus* gull (Pierotti and Annett 1995). Western Gulls are the most widely distributed and the second most abundant breeding seabird in southern California; large breeding colonies occur at San Miguel, Santa Barbara, Anacapa, and San

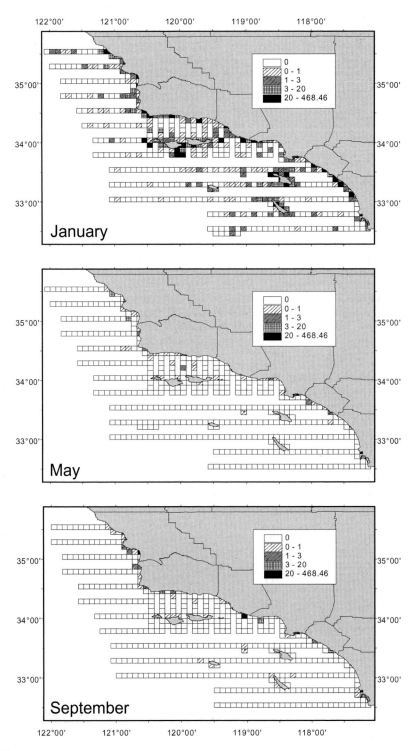

FIGURE 35. California Gull densities (birds/km²) and distribution off southern California from 1999–2002 during January, May, and September.

Nicolas islands (H. Carter, unpubl. data). In 1991, 14,000 breeding pairs were estimated to be in the SCB, a more than two-fold increase over the late 1970s (H. Carter, unpubl. data).

Briggs et al. (1987) observed Western Gulls along California coastlines in all months and seldom observed birds farther than 25 km seaward of the shelf break. In the SCB, Western Gulls were mostly restricted to areas near breeding colonies from April–August, but from September–February, they were distributed more evenly throughout the region (Briggs et al. 1987). In contrast, in 1999–2002 we observed Western Gulls throughout southern California in all seasons, on both at-sea and coastal surveys (Fig. 36). More than 96% of observed Western Gulls occurred <20 km from shore.

In 1999–2002, at-sea densities of Western Gulls did not differ among seasons but did differ among sub-areas (Table 5). We observed greatest densities in S3 in all months (Table 1c). Along coastlines, densities did not differ among sub-areas but did differ among seasons (Table 6). Mainland coastal densities were greatest in September and island coastal densities were greatest in January (Tables 2–4).

At-sea densities in 1999–2002 were greater than in 1975–1983 for the entire study area and S3, lower in S2, S4, and S5, and did not differ significantly in S1 (Tables 7a, 7b). Increased numbers apparently reflected increased breeding populations in the SCB, although some Western Gulls from central and northern California also winter in southern California and these populations have also increased (Penniman et al. 1990). Western Gulls also visit coastal lakes in the SCB and forage in garbage dumps, especially in winter, so many birds are not at sea. Western Gulls also roost when not foraging so we only measured actively feeding birds. In the breeding season, a large proportion of the population is at breeding colonies and not at sea. Many birds are seen near shore because they are commuting to colonies and roosting areas or rafting offshore of these areas.

Black-legged Kittiwake (Rissa tridactyla)

In the eastern Pacific, Black-legged Kittiwakes winter offshore from southern Alaska to central Baja California, Mexico (Baird 1994). Kittiwakes migrate south from their Alaskan breeding colonies in September and return north in March (Baird and Gould 1983). In 1975–1983, kittiwakes arrived in California waters in November, reached greatest densities from January through March, and departed in April and May (Briggs et al. 1987). Kittiwakes occurred from the coastline to 200 km from

shore and density did not decrease significantly with increasing distance from shore (Briggs et al. 1987). In January 2000–2002, kittiwakes occurred throughout the study area, except in the southeastern portion (S4). Birds were concentrated primarily <15 km from the northern Channel Islands and near San Nicolas Island (Fig. 37).

In 1999–2002, at-sea densities of kittiwakes did not differ significantly among sub-areas (Table 5). Densities were great only in January; we observed only four kittiwakes in May (2000) and none in September (Tables 1a–e). At-sea densities were greatest in S5, S2, and S1 (Tables 1a, 1b, 1e). We observed only 15 Black-legged Kittiwakes on coastal transects, all in January and all but two near the northern Channel Islands.

At-sea densities of Black-legged Kittiwakes were greater in 1975–1983 than in 1999–2002 for the entire study area, S1, S3, and S4, lower in S2, and did not differ significantly in S5 (Tables 7a, 7b). Population trends are difficult to assess because decline has been noted at some Alaskan colonies (Baird 1994) consistent with lower densities in 1999–2002.

Sabine's Gull (Xema sabini)

In the Pacific Ocean, Sabine's Gulls are seen off California during migrations between arctic nesting grounds and wintering areas off northern South America (Day et al. 2001). Briggs et al. (1987) recorded the species statewide from the shoreline to at least 200 km offshore; off southern California, they occurred seaward of the Santa Rosa-Cortes Ridge. In September 1999–2001, we observed Sabine's Gulls near Tanner and Cortez Banks (Fig. 38). In May and September, these gulls were observed north of Point Conception and west of San Miguel Island (Fig. 38).

At-sea densities did not differ significantly between May and September but did differ among sub-areas (Table 5). We observed greatest at-sea densities in S1 and lowest densities in S4 (Tables 1a, 1d). We did not observe Sabine's Gulls on coastal transects.

At-sea densities were greater in 1999–2002 than in 1975–1978 for the entire study area, S1, S2, S4, and S5 (Tables 7a, 7b).

Caspian Tern (Hydroprogne caspia)

Caspian Terns breed in widely dispersed locations on the shores of rivers, lakes, and marshes along the Pacific, Atlantic, and Gulf coasts. On the Pacific Coast, they winter from southern California to Guatemala (Cuthbert

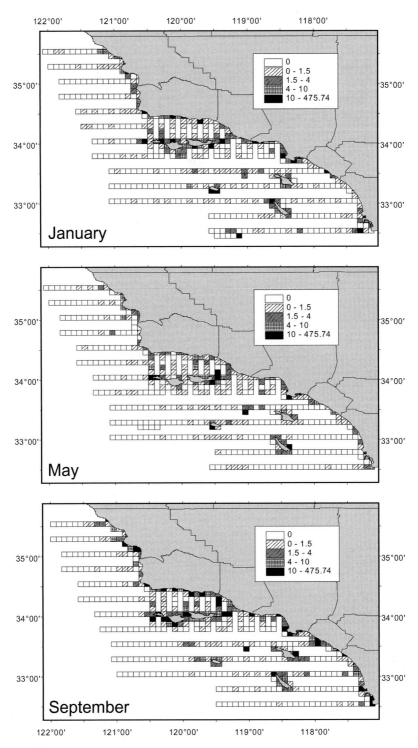

FIGURE 36. Western Gull densities (birds/km²) and distribution off southern California from 1999–2002 during January, May, and September.

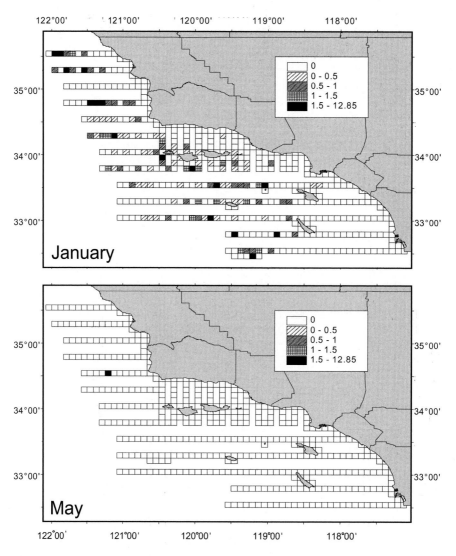

FIGURE 37. Black-legged Kittiwake densities (birds/km^2) and distribution off southern California from 1999–2002 during January and May.

and Wires 1999). In southern California, terns breed on salt pond levees in San Diego Bay (Gill and Mewaldt 1983). Pacific Coast populations have increased by >50% from 1984–1993 (Cuthbert and Wires 1999). In South San Diego Bay National Wildlife Refuge, an estimated 379 pairs of Caspian Terns bred in 2002 (USDI Fish and Wildlife Service 2005).

Briggs et al. (1987) recorded few terns because they did not conduct aerial surveys of coastlines, but they reported that Caspian Terns rarely occurred >1 km from shore. In 1999–2002, we consistently observed Caspian Terns on coastal transects near Point Loma, northern Santa Monica Bay, Santa Cruz Island, and south of Gaviota (Fig. 39). We observed only

16 Caspian Terns on at-sea transects and made no statistical comparisons. Coastal densities of Caspian Terns differed among seasons and sub-areas (Table 6). Greatest densities occurred in September and lowest densities in January (Tables 2–4).

ALCIDAE

Five alcid species commonly occur in southern California and were recorded throughout the study area except in coastal sub-area SMC (Fig. 40). At-sea densities differed among seasons and sub-areas with greatest densities in January in S1 and in May in S3 (Tables 1, 5). On coastal transects, densities differed among

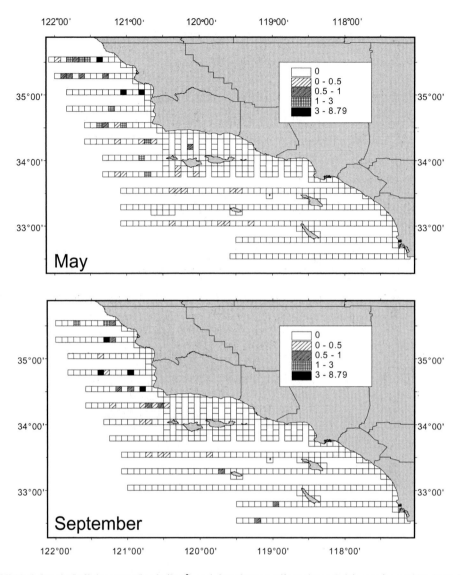

FIGURE 38. Sabine's Gull densities (birds/km²) and distribution off southern California from 1999–2002 during May and September. No Sabine's Gulls were observed during January.

seasons and four sub-areas where they occurred (NMC, CMC, NIC, and SIC) with greatest densities along the NIC, except in May when greatest densities occurred along the NMC (Tables 2–4, 6). At-sea densities of alcids were greater in 1975–1983 than in 1999–2002 for the entire study area and in each of the five sub-areas, but were not statistically significant for S3 (Tables 7a, 7b).

Common Murre (Uria aalge)

Along the eastern Pacific, Common Murres breed from the Bering Sea, Alaska, to Monterey County in central California (Ainley et al. 2002). Common Murres are the most abundant breeding seabird in California and Oregon (H. Carter, unpubl. data; Carter et al. 2001). Historically, Common Murres bred in the SCB on Prince Island, but as a result of egg gathering for private collections and possibly oil pollution, the colony was extirpated in 1912 (Carter et al. 2001). Common Murres generally winter from southern Alaska to southern California but have been observed as far south as central Baja California, Mexico. Birds occurring in southern California in winter likely originate from breeding populations in central California

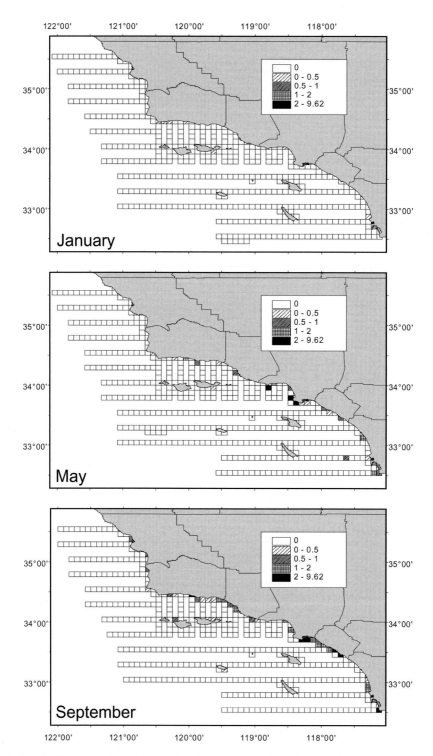

FIGURE 39. Caspian Tern densities (birds/km²) and distribution off southern California from 1999–2002 during January, May, and September.

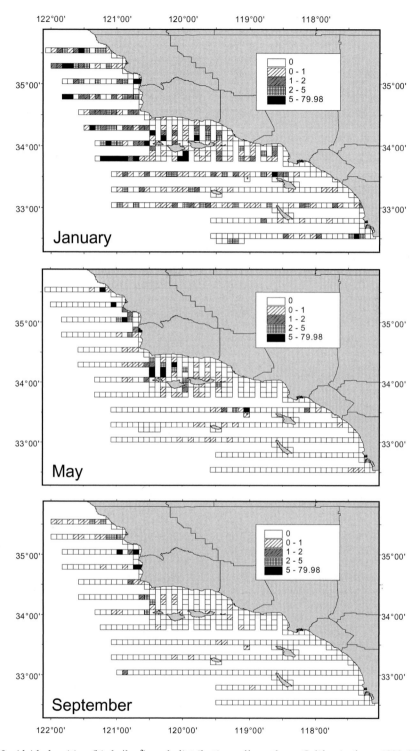

FIGURE 40. Alcid densities (birds/km²) and distribution off southern California from 1999–2002 during January, May, and September.

(Manuwal and Carter 2001). Central California breeding populations were increasing rapidly in the late 1970s but declined dramatically from 1982–1986 and continued to decline through 1989 (Takekawa et al. 1990, Carter et al. 2001). Declines in the breeding population were attributed mainly to mortality from gill-net fishing and oil spills, plus lesser impacts from reduced reproductive success associated with the severe 1982–1983 El Niño and human disturbance at breeding colonies (Takekawa et al. 1990; Carter et al. 2001, 2003). Since 1990, population recovery has been underway, reaching levels similar to 1980–1982 in the 1999–2002 period (G. McChesney, unpubl. data)

During the nesting season (April through July), Briggs et al. (1987) observed Common Murres in waters <150 m deep and 75% occurred <40 km from breeding colonies in central and northern California. In 1980–1983, they occurred south of Point Sur only outside of the nesting season, but even in the winter they were most abundant within 50 km of breeding colonies (Briggs et al. 1987). In 1975–1983, tens of thousands were estimated within Santa Barbara Channel and from Morro Bay to Point Arguello in the fall and winter (Briggs et al. 1987). In 1999–2002, we observed only 232 birds, and >85% were north of Point Conception (Fig. 41, Tables 1a–e). More than 90% of birds occurred <20 km from shore in waters <150 m deep.

Densities on at-sea transects in 1999–2002 differed among seasons and three sub-areas where Common Murres occurred (S1, S3, and S4; Table 5). At-sea densities were greatest in January and lowest in May (Tables 1a–e). We observed birds along coastal transects only in January (Tables 2–4). Most coastal sightings occurred near Morro Bay and Point Conception; one bird was observed near Santa Barbara Island (Fig. 41).

Despite substantial population recovery in central California, at-sea densities of Common Murres were statistically much lower in 1999–2002 than in 1975–1983 for the entire study area, S1, S3, and S4 (Tables 7a, 7b). Continued gill-net mortality of several thousand murres per year between Monterey and Morro bays in the late 1990s (Forney et al. 2001) may have reduced populations wintering in our study area, or central California populations may not have yet restored movements to southern California. Birds were observed in S2 and S5 in 1975–1983 but not in 1999–2002. For both studies, Common Murre densities were greatest in January, when partial colony attendance occurs in central California (Manuwal and Carter 2001).

Pigeon Guillemot (Cepphus columba)

Pigeon Guillemots breed on rocky shorelines and forage in nearby near-shore waters from the Bering Sea to Santa Barbara Island and range from northern Alaska to northwestern Mexico (Ewins 1993). In 1991, H. Carter (unpubl. data) estimated 1,600 breeding pairs to be in southern California, doubling the estimates for 1975–1978.

Briggs et al. (1987) observed Pigeon Guillemots mainly in June and July <2 km from shore and distributed from Santa Barbara Island to the Oregon border. We observed birds near Santa Barbara Island, between Santa Rosa and Santa Cruz islands, and along the mainland coast near Point Sal and Point Buchon; >92% occurred <2 km from shore (Fig. 42).

In 1999–2002, we recorded only seven Pigeon Guillemots on at-sea transects, all in May. Densities on coastal transects differed among seasons and the three sub-areas in which guillemots occurred (NMC, NIC, and SIC; Table 6). More than 89% of Pigeon Guillemot sightings occurred in May. We observed most birds along the NMC and NIC (Tables 3, 4). With so few at-sea observations in 1999–2002, we were unable to compare at-sea transect data with data from 1975–1983.

Xantus's Murrelet (Synthliboramphus hypoleucus)

The Xantus's Murrelet is one of the most southerly-distributed alcids with a limited breeding range extending from the SCB to central Baja California, Mexico (Drost and Lewis 1995). Of the two subspecies of Xantus's Murrelets, *S. h. scrippsi* nests in southern California and Baja California and *S. h. hypoleucus* nests primarily at Guadalupe Island, Mexico (Jehl and Bond 1975; Carter et al., in press). Both subspecies were recently listed by the state of California as threatened in 2004 and are listed as threatened in Mexico (E. Burkett, unpubl. data; Keitt, in press); they also have been petitioned for federal listing. Xantus's Murrelets breed on all Channel Islands except Santa Rosa and San Nicolas islands (Drost and Lewis 1995). In 1991, H. Carter (unpubl. data) estimated 700 breeding pairs at the largest known colony in the U.S. at Santa Barbara Island and considered this colony to be stable or declining slightly. Additional evidence of decline at SBI has been noted in later studies (W. Sydeman, unpubl. data; D. Whitworth, unpubl. data). Surveys in 1994–1996 found more widespread breeding in the SCB and higher breeding population estimates (E. Burkett, unpubl. data; H. Carter,

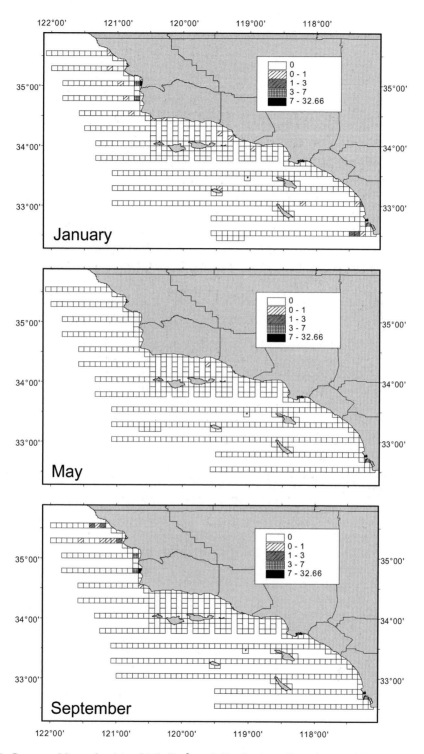

FIGURE 41. Common Murre densities (birds/km²) and distribution off southern California from 1999–2002 during January, May, and September.

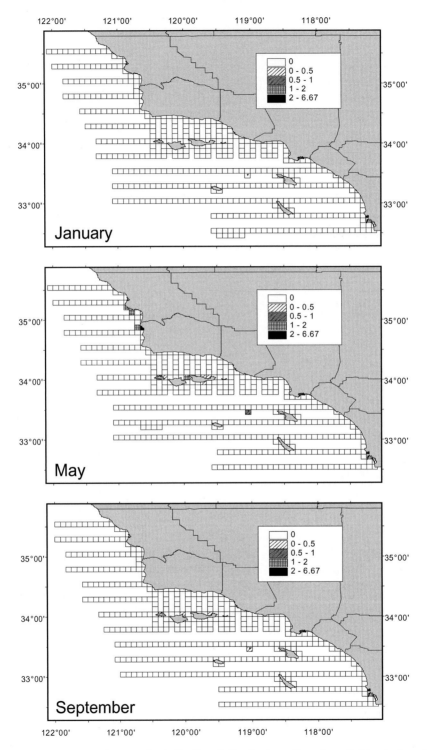

FIGURE 42. Pigeon Guillemot densities (birds/km²) and distribution off southern California from 1999–2002 during January, May, and September.

unpubl. data). Karnovsky et al. (2005) estimated about 8,000–16,000 birds in SCB in spring, corresponding to roughly 2,000–5,000 breeding pairs. Xantus's Murrelets may start attending breeding colonies in December or January (Murray et al. 1983, Gaston and Jones 1998).

Briggs et al. (1987) noted birds concentrated around Santa Barbara Island and off San Diego in the breeding months (March–May) with birds off San Diego presumably from the nearby Coronado Islands, Mexico. They were distributed north of Point Conception from August through October, 20–100 km from shore reflecting northward post-breeding dispersal (D. Whitworth, unpubl. data). In May in 1999–2001, greatest densities were near Santa Barbara and Anacapa islands and north of Point Conception along the coast; 88% of Xantus's Murrelets occurred <40 km from shore and correspondingly 87% occurred in depths <1,400 m (Fig. 43). Foraging near Anacapa Island was also noted during radio-telemetry studies in 1995–1997 and 2002–2003 (Whitworth et al. 2000, Hamilton 2005).

At-sea densities of Xantus's Murrelets did not differ significantly among sub-areas but did differ among seasons (Table 5). Their numbers were greatest in May with few birds observed in January or September (Tables 1a–e), suggesting that few birds had returned to colony areas by January in 2000–2002. Xantus's Murrelets were not observed on coastal transects in any month.

At-sea densities of Xantus's Murrelets were greater in 1999–2002 than in 1975–1983 for the entire study area, S1, and S5 (Tables 7a, 7b). Densities did not differ significantly in S3 or S4 (Tables 7a, 7b). Densities in S2 were not compared because birds were observed there only in 1999–2002. Karnovsky et al. (2005) found no trend between study periods from Point Conception to the Mexico border, although few birds were seen off San Diego. Given infrequent occurrence on surveys, higher densities may have reflected greater sampling effort near Santa Barbara and Anacapa islands.

Cassin's Auklet (Ptychoramphus aleuticus)

Cassin's Auklets are widely distributed in the Pacific Ocean, breeding from the Aleutian Islands, Alaska, to central Baja California, Mexico (Manuwal and Thoresen 1993). Cassin's Auklets are the third most abundant breeding species in southern California (H. Carter, unpubl. data). In 1991, the breeding population of Cassin's Auklets in the SCB was about 6,300 pairs, with >90% at San Miguel Island (Prince Island and Castle Rock) and the remainder at Santa Cruz and Santa Barbara islands (H. Carter, unpubl. data; Whitworth et al., in press). Numbers at Prince Island, the largest colony in the SCB, possibly declined between 1975–1978 and 1991, but differences in colony-based survey protocols and effort prevented assessment of population trends (H. Carter, unpubl. data).

In 1975–1983, Briggs et al. (1987) observed Cassin's Auklets year-round throughout California waters from the mid-continental shelf out to 150 km from shore, but in late spring and summer the species was concentrated near breeding colonies. From August through October, birds were distributed throughout the SCB west of San Clemente Island and over the continental shelf and slope from San Miguel Island to Point Buchon (Briggs et al. 1987). In 1999–2002, Cassin's Auklet distribution varied markedly with survey month, but birds generally were observed >10 km from shore (Fig. 44). In May, birds were concentrated in northwest Santa Barbara Channel and north of Point Conception, reflecting northward dispersal of SCB breeders (Adams et al. 2004). In September, most Cassin's Auklets were observed north of Point Conception. They were widely distributed across the SCB in January primarily west of San Nicolas Island. Limited colony attendance occurs in winter. Higher densities in January than May reflected incubating adults in May, juveniles at sea after the breeding season, and possibly some birds from the Farallon Islands feeding further south before regular colony attendance occurs pre-breeding. Like Briggs et al. (1987), we observed Cassin's Auklets primarily in deeper water seaward of the continental slope in September.

In 1999–2002, at-sea densities differed among seasons and sub-areas (Table 5). Overall, densities were greatest in January, whereas few birds were observed in September (Tables 1a–e). In May, densities were greatest in S3 near northern Channel Island breeding colonies (Table 1c). In January, densities were greatest in S2 (west of San Miguel Island) in waters averaging 1,450 m in depth (Table 1b). On coastline surveys, Cassin's Auklets only occurred near the northern Channel Islands where densities were greatest in January (Tables 2–4).

At-sea densities of Cassin's Auklets were greater in 1975–1983 than in 1999–2002 for the entire study area and S1, but lower in S3, S4, consistent with possible decline at the largest breeding colony at Prince Island (Tables 7a, 7b). Numbers of breeding birds at colonies at Santa Cruz and Santa Barbara islands declined since 1991 (J. Adams, unpubl. data). At-sea densities did not differ significantly in S2 (Tables 7a).

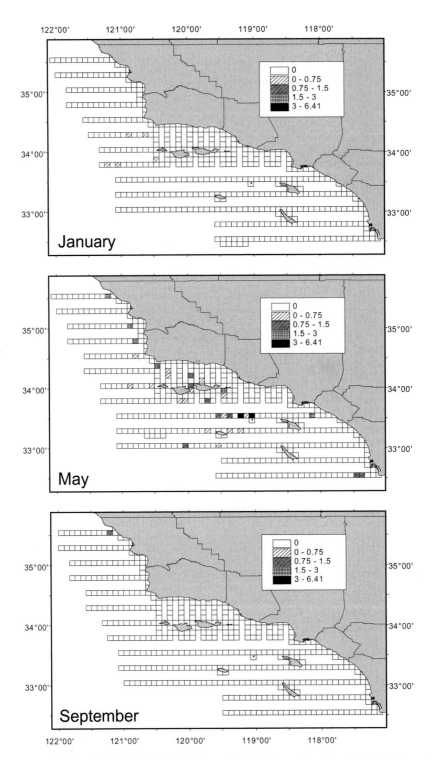

FIGURE 43. Xantus's Murrelet densities (birds/km²) and distribution off southern California from 1999–2002 during January, May, and September.

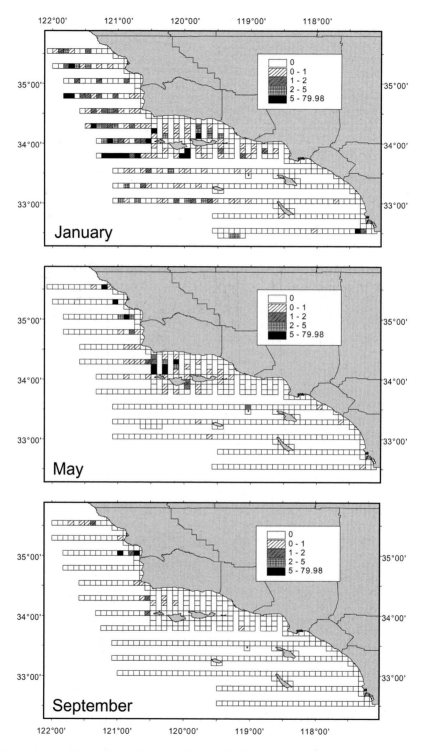

FIGURE 44. Cassin's Auklet densities (birds/km²) and distribution off southern California from 1999–2002 during January, May, and September.

Rhinoceros Auklet (Cerorhinca monocerata)

Rhinoceros Auklets breed from the Aleutian Islands, Alaska to San Miguel Island. Birds winter from southeast Alaska to southern Baja California, Mexico (Gaston and Dechesne 1996). In 1991, small numbers of Rhinoceros Auklets were found to breed at San Miguel Island and north of Point Conception, six small breeding colonies also were observed (H. Carter, unpubl. data; McChesney et al. 1995). The California breeding population was estimated to be 900 breeding pairs representing a five-fold increase over 1979–1980 (H. Carter, unpubl. data).

In 1975–1978, Rhinoceros Auklet densities in the SCB were lowest in the summer and greatest in January, February, and March (Briggs et al. 1987). In spring, birds occurred along the western margin of the SCB, in the passages between the northern Channel Islands, and along the shelfbreak from Point Arguello to Oregon (Briggs et al. 1987). In 1999–2002 in January, we observed Rhinoceros Auklets throughout southern California <100 km from shore (Fig. 45). Small numbers observed in May and September occurred near breeding colonies in the northern Channel Islands or north of Point Conception.

At-sea densities differed among seasons and sub-areas (Table 5). Rhinoceros Auklet densities were greatest in January and much lower in May and September (Tables 1a–e). In all months, at-sea densities were greatest in S1, lowest in S2, and intermediate in S3, S4, and S5 (Tables 1a–e). We observed only five Rhinoceros Auklets on coastal transects in 1999–2002, all near the northern Channel Islands. At-sea densities of Rhinoceros Auklets in 1975–1983 were greater than densities in 1999–2002 in the entire study area, S2, and S3, but were lower in S1 (Tables 7a, 7b). At-sea densities did not differ significantly in S4 or S5 (Tables 7b). Not consistent with lower densities in 1999–2002, populations on the west coast of North America have increased in recent years (Ainley et al. 1994, Gaston and Dechesne 1996).

Tufted Puffin (Fratercula cirrhata)

Tufted Puffins breed from California to the Bering and Chukchi seas, extending to Japan (Gaston and Jones 1998). Tufted Puffins did not breed in the SCB from 1912–1991, but small numbers were found breeding at Prince Island in 1991 and 1994 (H. Carter, unpubl. data; McChesney et al. 1995). At the Farallon Islands off San Francisco, California, puffins experienced a population decline from 1,000s of birds in the late 1800s to an estimated 100 breeders in

1982. Although their winter distribution is not well known, Tufted Puffins generally spend the winter well offshore and Briggs et al. (1987) found puffins most abundant off California in January, April, and May. During periods of annual maximum abundance in the winter and spring in 1975–1978, low thousands were estimated in the SCB (Briggs et al. 1987). Since few puffins breed south of British Columbia, these birds must have originated from British Columbia or Alaska.

We did not observe Tufted Puffins during our study. In the winter, we may have misidentified small numbers of Tufted Puffins as Rhinoceros Auklets but our population estimates still would be much lower than found by Briggs et al. (1987). We suggest that puffins were not migrating to southern California in 1999–2002, consistent with major declines in populations from southeast Alaska to California (Piatt and Kitaysky 2002).

DISCUSSION

In 1999–2002, we examined distribution and abundance of seabirds off southern California from Cambria to the Mexican border with the first comprehensive aerial surveys in two decades. Earlier surveys in 1975–1983 (Briggs et al. 1987) focused on describing temporal patterns of seabird abundance in at-sea habitats, with monthly surveys limited to a relatively small area that excluded coastal habitats in the SCB. In 1999–2002, we focused on completing: (1) better assessment of seabird abundance in five at-sea and five coastal sub-areas during 3 mo (May, September, and January); and (2) comparison of seabird abundance in these 3 mo for at-sea sub-areas between 1999–2002 and 1975–1983 to assess general trends.

While our study design was directed at reducing variability between our study and Briggs et al. (1987), we flew similar, but not identical, transect lines. Our effort within the SCB was greater than Briggs et al. (1987), and we concentrated effort around the northern Channel Islands. Aircraft type and observers differed between the two studies, and we sampled intensively during 3 mo of the year, whereas Briggs et al. (1987) sampled year-round. Thus, although they were more likely to record annual peaks in abundance, we averaged their survey data across months (April–June) to reduce variation in peak abundance between studies. However, we used the same analytical approach to estimate densities from both datasets to derive comparable estimates.

While direct comparisons are complicated by these differences in survey coverage, our

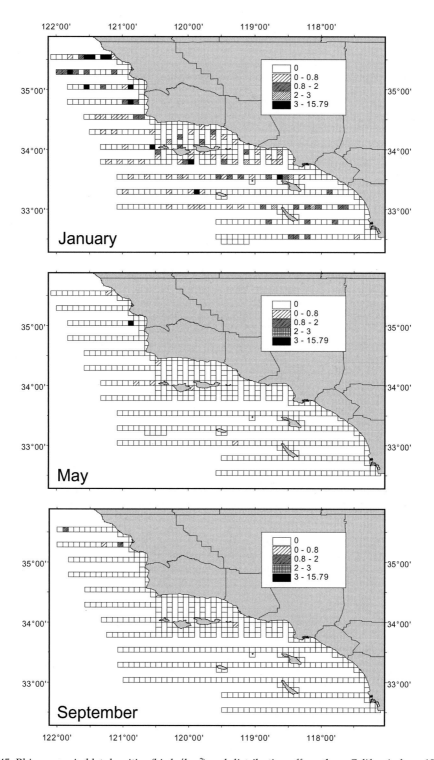

FIGURE 45. Rhinoceros Auklet densities (birds/km²) and distribution off southern California from 1999–2002 during January, May, and September.

statistical comparisons indicate that for all sea-birds combined, a definite decline in abundance has occurred in the SCB from 1975–1983 to 1999–2002. We estimated average densities of 11.3 seabirds/km^2 on at-sea transects and 70.9 seabirds/km^2 on coastal transects, while Briggs et al. (1987) estimated densities of 110 seabirds/km^2 over the continental shelf. In 1999–2002, total seabird abundance was 14% lower in January, 57% lower in May, and 42% lower in September than in the earlier study.

Species with dramatically decreased densi-ties included the Common Murre (≥75% decline in each season), Sooty Shearwater (55% in May and 27% in September), and Bonaparte's Gull (≥95% in each season). Compared with Briggs et al. (1987), we observed significantly lower densities of Sooty Shearwaters in the SCB in May and September. Many researchers have noted recent declines in Sooty Shearwater abundance throughout the CCS (Veit et al. 1996, 1997; Oedekoven et al. 2001, Hyrenbach and Veit 2003). Reasons for this apparent decline are unclear but Spear and Ainley (1999) hypoth-esized that Sooty Shearwaters had changed their migration routes in response to a cooling trend in the central North Pacific resulting in a distribution shift and reduction in the CCS. However, declines at breeding colonies also have been noted in recent years, indicating a more general effect in decline possibly associ-ated with larger forces such as global change.

Common Murres, the most abundant breed-ing seabird species in California, were season-ally abundant in the SCB in 1975–1978 (Briggs et al. 1987), but we rarely observed them during this study. Murre densities were significantly lower in all sub-areas compared with Briggs et al. (1987). Decline in Common Murre num-bers in southern California may reflect earlier decline in the central California breeding popu-lation in the 1980s (Takekawa et al. 1990, Carter et al. 2001). Factors contributing to this decline included gill netting, oil spills, and effects from the 1982–1983 El Niño event (Takekawa et al. 1990). Central California breeding popula-tions recovered to a great extent prior to 1999, but they may not have redeveloped wintering movements to the SCB. Decline in Bonaparte Gull numbers is difficult to assess because of a lack of historical data due to their remote breed-ing habits and poor enumeration of wintering populations (Burger and Gochfeld 2002).

Conversely, ten species were more abundant in 1999–2002 than in 1975–1983. Brown Pelicans (167% overall), Xantus's Murrelets (125% over-all), Cassin's Auklets (100% overall), Ashy Storm-Petrels (450% overall) and Western Gulls (55% in May), and Brandt's Cormorants (450%

in September) were among the most notable species with increased densities. All six of these species also breed in the SCB. Brown Pelicans have responded positively with increased local breeding populations since the mid-1970s, pos-sibly related to reduced DDE concentrations in the SCB. However, increasing populations in the Gulf of California, which migrate into SCB waters after breeding, are primarily responsible for the Brown Pelican increases that we found. Higher numbers of Xantus's Murrelets may reflect changes in at-sea distribution and sur-vey differences, since a Pacific Coast analysis indicated no significant change in at-sea popu-lation size (Karnovsky et al. 2005). Even though a decline has been noted at Santa Barbara Island (H. Carter, unpubl. data; W. Sydeman, unpubl. data; D. Whitworth, unpubl. data), an increase is suspected at the Coronado Islands (D. Whitworth, unpubl. data) and trends at other colonies are poorly known. For Cassin's Auklets, colony declines have been found in the SCB, the South Farallon Islands, and Triangle Island, British Columbia, which may suggest that increased numbers on our 1999–2002 surveys rep-resent differences in survey coverage. Similarly, little change in Ashy Storm-Petrel numbers at SCB colonies may suggest that increases we recorded reflect survey differences. However, increased numbers of Western Gulls and Brandt's Cormorants likely represent increased breeding populations in southern California.

For seasonal visitors such as Western Grebes, Surf Scoters, and loons, abundance increased in the SCB but decreased north of Point Conception. A similar pattern was found dur-ing limited aerial surveys conducted in 1996–1997 (Pierson et al. 2000). Recent aerial and boat surveys in Puget Sound, Washington, have indicated a 95% decline in Western Grebes, 57% decline in Surf Scoters, and 79% decline in loons over a 20-yr period (D. Nysewander, unpubl. data). Thus, increased numbers in the SCB may indicate a southern shift in distribution of these over-wintering populations. The lack of SCB aerial coastal surveys in 1975–1978 likely led to under-representation of these coastal species in the past.

The SCB has been described as a complex transition zone for cold and warm temperate biotas, partly because this is where colder, up-welled waters from north of Point Conception meet warmer waters of sub-tropical origin (Horn and Allen 1978, Murray and Littler 1981). Recent studies have indicated a blur-ring of this line as some marine species from warmer-water masses have recently expanded their ranges north of Point Conception (Stepien and Rosenblatt 1991, Sagarin et al. 1999). Similar factors may be affecting the distributions of seabirds. Ainley et al. (1994, 1996) demonstrated an inverse relationship between seabird reproductive success and ocean temperature at the Farallon Islands. However, locally breeding seabirds are tied to feeding in SCB waters due to their breeding colony locations on the Channel Islands, Coronado Islands, and along the mainland coast from Cambria to Point Conception (Sowls et al. 1980, H. Carter, unpubl. data). Thus, it is not possible for these birds to shift their feeding areas to a great degree, unless they also change breeding colonies which does not occur frequently. Recent increases in local breeding populations, even during warm periods, indicate that the SCB may be able to buffer changes in ocean temperature and the associated effects.

Three severe El Niño events (1982–1983, 1992–1993, and 1997–1998) occurred between the 1975–1978 and 1999–2002 survey periods. Severe El Niño events cause poor reproduction and high adult mortality of certain locally-breeding seabirds (and greater mortality for some visiting species) while others are not affected. Our surveys began in May 1999, 2 yr after the 1997–1998 El Niño event. The 1999–2002 period featured a series of cold water La Niña events which led some researchers to postulate that the CCS had undergone a fundamental climate shift, on the scale of those documented in the 1920s, mid 1940s, and mid 1970s (Schwing et al. 2002). While La Niñas often follow El Niños (Ainley and Boekelheide 1990), these La Niña events have corresponded with generally stronger than normal upwelling in the CCS and have generated the greatest 4-yr mean upwelling index value on record (Schwing et al. 2002). Briggs et al. (1987) conducted 1975–1978 surveys during another climate shift leading to increased temperatures throughout the CCS (Mantua et al. 1997). They surveyed north of Point Conception in 1980–1983 after a transition to warmer water had occurred in the California Current, when negative effects of the warmer water on seabird abundances might have occurred. Still, overall numbers were greater, indicating that ocean temperatures are not entirely responsible for trends in seabird abundances.

Recently, the health of coastal oceans has been highlighted as a major issue of concern (U.S. Commission on Ocean Policy 2004). In addition to continuing impacts from DDT and PCB contamination and oil pollution, increased urbanization in southern California may be threatening the health of the SCB through runoff and increased use of marine resources. Since the 1975–1983 aerial surveys, the human population has increased by >10 million in California and >25% in the Los Angeles region (Censusscope 2005). Seabirds are sensitive indicators of change in the marine environment due to both natural and anthropogenic factors (Bost and Le Maho 1993, Ainley et al. 1996, Jones et al. 2002). Changes in seabird populations may be warning signs for environmental degradation caused by coastal development, as well as for larger forces that alter marine systems such as climate change. Thus, periodic at-sea surveys of seabirds, with direct comparison to past studies, may provide an effective indication of how well, or how poorly, we are managing and conserving our coastal marine resources.

ACKNOWLEDGMENTS

This research was funded by the U.S. Geological Survey, Science Support Program at the request of the Minerals Management Service, Pacific Outer Continental Shelf Region. Humboldt State University Sponsored Projects Foundation greatly facilitated project administration. Significant additional funding and logistical support were provided by the U.S. Navy, and permits and logistical support were provided by Channel Islands National Park and Channel Islands National Marine Sanctuary. We thank Aspen Helicopters for their aircraft and expert pilots R. Throckmorton and B. Hansen. We thank K. Ellsworth for assisting in creating distribution maps, T. James for reformatting figures and tables, and Minerals Management Service and the University of California at Santa Barbara for providing interns to enter data. We give special thanks to L. Thorsteinson, S. Schwartz, and T. Keeney for project support and G. Ford and L. Stauss for critical project assistance. Valuable comments were provided by J. Adams, S. Allen, I. Woo, K. Phillips, L. Spear, R. Veit, W. Tyler, and an anonymous reviewer. This monograph is dedicated to the memory of our colleague, Mark Pierson.

LITERATURE CITED

ADAMS, J., J. Y. TAKEKAWA, AND H. R. CARTER. 2004. Foraging distance and home range of Cassin's Auklets nesting at two colonies in the California Channel Islands. Condor 106:618–637.

AINLEY, D. G. 1976. The occurrence of seabirds in the coastal region of California. Western Birds 7: 33–68.

AINLEY, D. G. 1995. Ashy Storm-Petrel (*Oceanodroma homochroa*). *In* A. Poole, and F. Gill (editors). The Birds of North America, No. 185. The Academy of Natural Sciences, Philadelphia, PA, and the American Ornithologists' Union, Washington, DC.

AINLEY, D. G., AND R. J. BOEKELHEIDE. 1990. Seabirds of the Farallon Islands: ecology and dynamics in an upwelling-system community. Stanford University Press, Palo Alto, CA.

AINLEY, D. G., D. N. NETTLESHIP, H. R. CARTER, AND A. E. STOREY. 2002. Common Murre (*Uria aalge*). *In* A. Poole, and F. Gill (editors). The Birds of North America, No. 666. The Academy of Natural Sciences, Philadelphia, PA, and the American Ornithologists' Union, Washington, DC.

AINLEY, D. G., G. S. STRONG, T. M. PENNIMAN, AND R. J. BOEKELHEIDE. 1990. The feeding ecology of Farallon seabirds. Pp. 51–127 *in* D. G. Ainley, and R. J. Boekelheide (editors). Seabirds of the Farallon Islands, ecology, dynamics, and structure of an upwelling community. Stanford University Press, Palo Alto, CA.

AINLEY, D. G., W. J. SYDEMAN, AND J. NORTON. 1996. Apex predators indicate interannual negative and positive anomalies in the California current food web. Marine Ecology Progress Series 137:1–10.

AINLEY, D. G., W. J. SYDEMAN, S. A. HATCH, AND U. W. WILSON. 1994. Seabird population trends along the West Coast of North America; causes and extent of regional concordance. Studies in Avian Biology 15:119–133.

ANDERSON, D. W., AND F. GRESS. 1983. Status of a northern population of California Brown Pelicans. Condor 85:79–88.

ANDERSON, D. W., AND I. T. ANDERSON. 1976. Distribution and status of Brown Pelicans in the California current. American Birds 30:3–12.

ANDERSON, D. W., J. R. JEHL, JR., R. W. RISEBROUGH, L. A. WOODS, L. R. DEWEESE, AND W. G. EDGECOMB. 1975. Brown Pelicans: improved reproduction off the southern California coast. Science 190:806–808.

ANDERSON, D. W., D. J. REISH, R. B. SPIES, M. E. BRADY, AND E. W. SEGELHORST. 1993. Human impacts. Pp. 682–766 *in* M. D Dailey, D. J. Reish, and J. W. Anderson (editors). Ecology of the Southern California Bight: a synthesis and interpretation. University of California Press, Berkeley, CA.

BAIRD, P. H. 1993. Birds. Pp. 541–603 *in* M. D Dailey, D. J. Reish, and J. W. Anderson (editors). Ecology of the Southern California Bight: a synthesis and interpretation. University of California Press, Berkeley, CA.

BAIRD, P. H. 1994. Black-legged Kittiwake (*Rissa tridactyla*). *In* A. Poole, and F. Gill (editors). The Birds of North America, No. 92. The Academy of Natural Sciences, Philadelphia, PA, and The American Ornithologists' Union, Washington, DC.

BAIRD, P. H., AND P. GOULD. 1983. The breeding biology and feeding ecology of marine birds in the Gulf of Alaska. USDC, NOAA OCSEAP Final Report 45 (1986):121–505.

BIRDLIFE INTERNATIONAL. 2003. BirdLife's online World bird database: the site for bird conservation. Version 2.0. BirdLife International, Cambridge, UK. <http://www.birdlife.org> (14 August 2006).

BOST, C. A., AND Y. LE MAHO. 1993. Seabirds as bioindicators of changing marine ecosystems: new perspectives. Acta Oecologica 14:463–470.

BRIGGS, K. T., AND E. W. CHU. 1986. Sooty Shearwaters off California: distribution, abundance, and habitat use. Condor 88:355–364.

BRIGGS, K .T., D. B. LEWIS, W. B. TYLER, AND G. L. HUNT, JR. 1981. Brown Pelicans in southern California: habitat use and environmental fluctuations. Condor 83:1–15.

BRIGGS, K. T., W. B. TYLER, AND D. B. LEWIS. 1985a. Comparison of ship and aerial surveys of birds at sea. Journal of Wildlife Management 49: 405-411.

BRIGGS, K. T., W. B. TYLER, AND D. B. LEWIS. 1985b. Aerial surveys for seabirds: methodological experiments. Journal of Wildlife Management 49: 412-417.

BRIGGS, K. T., W. B. TYLER, D. B. LEWIS, AND D. R. CARLSON. 1987. Bird communities at sea off California, 1975–1983. Studies in Avian Biology 11:1–74.

BRIGGS, K. T., W. B. TYLER, D. B. LEWIS, P. R. KELLY, AND D. A. CROLL. 1983. Brown Pelicans in central and northern California. Journal of Field Ornithology 54:353–373.

BROOKE, M. 2004. Albatrosses and petrels across the world. Oxford University Press, Oxford, UK.

BURGER, A. E., AND D. M. FRY. 1993. Effects of oil pollution on seabirds in the northeast Pacific. Pages 254–263 *in* K. Vermeer, K. T. Briggs, K. H. Morgan, and D. Siegel-Causey (editors). The status, ecology, and conservation of marine birds of the North Pacific. Special Publication, Canadian Wildlife Service, Ottawa, ON, Canada.

BURGER, J., AND M. GOCHFELD. 2002. Bonaparte's Gull (*Larus philadelphia*). *In* A. Poole, and F. Gill (editors). The Birds of North America, No. 634. The

Academy of Natural Sciences, Philadelphia, PA, and the American Ornithologists' Union, Washington, DC.

BURNESS, G. P., K. LEFEVRE, AND C. T. COLLINS. 1999. Elegant Tern (*Sterna elegans*). *In* A. Poole, and F. Gill (editors). The Birds of North America, No. 404. The Academy of Natural Sciences, Philadelphia, PA; and the American Ornithologists' Union, Washington, DC.

CAMPBELL, R. W., N. K. DAWE, I. McTAGGART-COWAN, J. M. COOPER, G. W. KAISER, AND M. C. E. McNALL. 1990. The birds of British Columbia. Volume 2. Royal British Columbia Museum, Victoria, BC, Canada.

CARTER, H. R. 2003. Oil and California's seabirds: an overview. Marine Ornithology 31:1–7.

CARTER, H. R., V. A. LEE, G. W. PAGE, M. W. PARKER, R. G. FORD, G. SWARTZMAN, S. W. KRESS, B. R. SISKIN, S. W. SINGER, AND D. M. FRY. 2003. The Apex Houston oil spill in central California: seabird injury assessment and litigation process. Marine Ornithology 31:9–19.

CARTER, H. R., S. G. SEALY, E. E. BURKETT, AND J. F. PIATT. 2005. Biology and conservation of the Xantus's Murrelet: discovery, taxonomy, and distribution. Marine Ornithology 33:81–87.

CARTER, H. R., A. R. SOWLS, M. S. RODWAY, U. W. WILSON, R. W. LOWE, G. J. McCHESNEY, F. GRESS, AND D. W. ANDERSON. 1995. Population size, trends, and conservation problems of the Double-crested Cormorant on the Pacific Coast of North America. Colonial Waterbirds 18 (Special Publication 1): 189–215.

CARTER, H. R., D. L. WHITWORTH, J. Y. TAKEKAWA, T. W. KEENEY, AND P. R. KELLY. 2000. At-sea threats to Xantus' Murrelets (*Synthliboramphus hypoleucus*) in the Southern California Bight. Pp. 435–447 *in* D. R. Browne, K. L. Mitchell, and H. W. Chaney (editors). Proceedings of the Fifth California Islands symposium. U.S. Minerals Management Service, Camarillo, CA.

CARTER, H. R., U. W. WILSON, R. W. LOWE, M. S. RODWAY, D. A. MANUWAL, J. E. TAKEKAWA, AND J. L. YEE. 2001. Population trends of the Common Murre (*Uria aalge californica*). Pp. 33–132 *in* D. A. Manuwal, H. R. Carter, T. S. Zimmerman, and D. L. Orthmeyer (editors). Biology and conservation of the Common Murre in California, Oregon, Washington, and British Columbia. Volume 1: Natural history and population trends. U.S. Geological Survey Information Technical Report USGS/BRD/ITR-2000-0012, Washington, DC.

CENSUSSCOPE. 2005. Los Angeles-Long Beach, California population growth. <http://www.censusscope.org/us/m4480/chart_popl.html> (16 October 2006).

CHELTON, D. B. 1984. Seasonal variability of alongshore-geostrophic velocity off central California. Journal of Geophysical Research 89(C3):3473–3486.

CHILTON, G., AND S. G. SEALY. 1987. Species roles in mixed-feeding flocks of seabirds. Journal of Field Ornithology 58:456–463.

CUTHBERT, F. J., AND L. R. WIRES. 1999. Caspian Tern (*Sterna caspia*). *In* A. Poole, and F. Gill (editors). The Birds of North America, No. 403. The Academy of Natural Sciences, Philadelphia, PA, and The American Ornithologists' Union, Washington, DC.

DAILEY, M. D., J. W. ANDERSON, D. J. REISH, AND D. S. GORSLINE. 1993. The Southern California Bight: background and setting. Pp. 1–18 *in* M. D. Dailey, D. J. Reish, and J. W. Anderson (editors), Ecology of the Southern California Bight: a synthesis and interpretation. University of California Press, Berkeley, CA.

DAY, R. H., I. J. STENHOUSE, AND H. G. GILCHRIST. 2001. Sabine's Gull (*Xema sabini*). *In* A. Poole, and F. Gill (editors). The Birds of North America, No. 634. The Academy of Natural Sciences, Philadelphia, PA, and the American Ornithologists' Union, Washington, DC.

DENNER, W. D., D. R. SIDES, J. C. MUELLER, L. C. BREAKER, AND K. T. BRIGGS. 1988. Final report California seabird ecology study. Volume II. Satellite data analysis. Publication PB89-126692, U.S. Department of Commerce, National Technical Information Service, Springfield, VA.

DROST, C. A., AND D. B. LEWIS. 1995. Xantus' Murrelet (*Synthliboramphus hypoleucus*). *In* A. Poole, and F. Gill (editors). The Birds of North America, No. 164. The Academy of Natural Sciences, Philadelphia, PA, and The American Ornithologists' Union, Washington, DC.

EVERETT, W. T. 1988. Biology of the Black-vented Shearwater. Western Birds 19:89–104.

EVERETT, W. T., AND D. W. ANDERSON. 1991. Status and conservation of the breeding seabirds on offshore Pacific islands of Baja California and the Gulf of California. Pp. 115–140 *in* J. P. Croxall (editor). Seabird status and conservation: a supplement. Technical Publication Number 11. International Council Bird Preservation, Cambridge, UK.

EVERETT, W. T., AND R. L. PITMAN. 1993. Status and conservation of shearwaters in the North Pacific. Pp. 93–100 *in* K. Vermeer, K. T. Briggs, K. H. Morgan, and D. Siegel-Causey (editors). The status, ecology, and conservation of marine birds of the North Pacific. Special Publication. Canadian Wildlife Service, Ottawa, ON, Canada.

EWINS, P. J. 1993. Pigeon Guillemot (*Cepphus columba*). *In* A. Poole, and F. Gill (editors). The Birds of North America, No. 49. The Academy of Natural Sciences, Philadelphia, PA, and The American Ornithologists' Union, Washington, DC.

FORNEY, K. A., S. R. BENSON, AND G. A. CAMERON. 2001. Central California gillnet effort and bycatch of sensitive species, 1900–1998. Pp. 141–160 *in* Proceedings—seabird bycatch: trends, roadblocks, and solutions. University of Alaska Sea Grant. AK-SG-01-01. Fairbanks, AK.

GASTON, A. J., AND I. L. JONES. 1998. The Auks, Alcidae. Oxford University Press, Inc., New York, NY.

GASTON, A. J., AND S. B. C. DECHESNE. 1996. Rhinoceros Auklet (Cerorhinca monocerata). In A. Poole, and F. Gill (editors). The Birds of North America, No. 212. The Academy of Natural Sciences, Philadelphia, PA, and The American Ornithologists' Union, Washington, DC.

GILL, R. E., AND L. R. MEWALDT. 1983. Pacific Coast Caspian Terns—dynamics of an expanding population. Auk 100:369–381.

GRESS, F., AND D. W. ANDERSON. 1983. The California Brown Pelican recovery plan. USDI Fish and Wildlife Service, Portland, OR.

GRESS, F., R. W. RISEBROUGH, D. W. ANDERSON, L. F. KIFF, AND J. R. JEHL, JR. 1973. Reproductive failures of Double-crested Cormorants in southern California and Baja California. Wilson Bulletin 85:197–208.

GUICKING, D., D. RISTOW, P. H. BECKER, R. SCHLATTER, P. BERTHOLD, AND U. QUERNER. 2001. Satellite tracking of the Pink-footed Shearwater in Chile. Waterbirds 24:8–15.

HAMILTON, C. D. 2005. At sea distribution, habitat, and foraging behavior of Xantus's Murrelets (Synthliboramphus hypoleucus) during the breeding season in the Southern California Bight. M.S. thesis, Humboldt State University, Arcata, CA.

HARMS, S., AND C. D. WINANT. 1998. Characteristic patterns of the circulation in the Santa Barbara Channel. Journal of Geophysical Research 103(C2):3041–3065.

HARRISON, P. 1983. Seabirds: an identification guide. Houghton Mifflin Co., Boston, MA.

HATCH, S. A., AND D. N. NETTLESHIP. 1998. Northern Fulmar (Fulmarus glacialis). In A. Poole, and F. Gill (editors). The Birds of North America, No. 361. The Academy of Natural Sciences, Philadelphia, PA, and the American Ornithologists' Union, Washington, DC.

HATCH, S. A., AND D. V. WESELOH. 1999. Double-crested Cormorant (Phalacrocorax auritus). In A. Poole, and F. Gill (editors). The Birds of North America, No. 441. The Academy of Natural Sciences, Philadelphia, PA, and the American Ornithologists' Union, Washington, DC.

HICKEY, B. M. 1993. Physical oceanography. Pp 19–70 in M. D. Dailey, D. J. Reish, and J. W. Anderson (editors), Ecology of the southern California bight: a synthesis and interpretation. University of California Press, Berkeley, CA.

HOBSON, K. A. 1997. Pelagic Cormorant (Phalacrocorax pelagicus). In A. Poole, and F. Gill (editors). The Birds of North America, No. 282. The Academy of Natural Sciences, Philadelphia, PA, and The American Ornithologists' Union, Washington, DC.

HORN, M. H., AND L. G. ALLEN. 1978. A distributional analysis of California coastal marine fishes. Journal of Biogeography 5:23–42.

HOWELL, N. G., AND S. WEBB. 1995. A guide to the birds of Mexico and northern Central America. Oxford University Press, New York, NY.

HUNT, G. L., R. L. PITMAN, AND H. L. JONES. 1980. Distribution and abundance of seabirds breeding on the California Channel Islands. Pp. 443–459 in D. M. Power (editor). The California Islands: proceedings of a multidisciplinary symposium. Santa Barbara Museum Natural History, Santa Barbara, CA.

HUNTINGTON, C. E., R. G. BUTLER, AND R. A. MAUCK. 1996. Leach's Storm-Petrel (Oceanodroma leucorhoa). In A. Poole, and F. Gill (editors). The Birds of North America, No. 233. The Academy of Natural Sciences, Philadelphia, PA, and The American Ornithologists' Union, Washington, DC.

HYRENBACH, K. D., AND R. R. VEIT. 2003. Ocean warming and seabird communities of the southern California current system (1987–1998): response at multiple temporal scales. Deep Sea Research II 50:2537–2565.

JAQUES, D. L. 1994. Range expansion and roosting ecology of non-breeding California Brown Pelicans. M.S. thesis, University of California, Davis, CA.

JAQUES, D. L., C. S. STRONG, AND T. W. KEENEY. 1996. Brown Pelican roosting patterns and response to disturbance at Mugu Lagoon and other non-breeding sites in the Southern California Bight. National Biological Service, Technical Report Number 54, Tuscon, AZ.

JEHL, J. R., JR. 1973. Studies of a declining population of Brown Pelicans in northwestern Baja California. Condor 75:69–79.

JEHL, J. R., JR., AND S. I. BOND. 1975. Morphological variation and species limits of the genus Endomychura. Transactions of the San Diego Society of Natural History 18:9–24.

JOHNSGARD, P. A. 1981. The plovers, sandpipers, and snipes of the world. University of Nebraska Press, Lincoln, NE.

JONES, I., F. M. HUNTER, AND G. J. ROBERTSON. 2002. Annual adult survival of Least Auklets (Aves: Alcidae) varies with large-scale climatic conditions of the North Pacific Ocean. Oecologia 133:38–44.

KARNOVSKY, N. J., L. B. SPEAR, H. R. CARTER, D. G. AINLEY, K. D. AMEY, L. T. BALLANCE, K. T. BRIGGS, R. G. FORD, G. L. HUNT, JR., C. KEIPER, J. W. MASON, K. H. MORGAN, R.L. PITMAN AND C. T. TYNAN. 2005. At-sea distribution, abundance and habitat affinities of Xantus's Murrelets. Marine Ornithology 33:89–104.

KEITH, J. O., L. A. WOODS, JR., AND E. G. HUNT. 1971. Reproductive failure in Brown Pelicans on the Pacific Coast. Transactions of the North American Wildlife and Natural Resources Conference 35:56–63.

KEITT, B. S. 2005 Current status of Xantus's Murrelets *Synthliboramphus hypoleucus* and their nesting habitat in Baja California, Mexico. Marine Ornithology 33:105–114.

KEITT, B. S., B. R. TERSCHY, AND D. A. CROLL. 2000. Black-vented Shearwater (*Puffinus opisthomelas*). *In* A. Poole, and F. Gill (editors). The Birds of North America, No. 521. The Academy of Natural Sciences, Philadelphia, PA, and The American Ornithologists' Union, Washington, DC.

LEHMAN, P. E. 1994. The birds of Santa Barbara County, California. University of California, Santa Barbara, CA.

LYNN, R. J., AND J. J. SIMPSON. 1987. The California current system: The seasonal variability of its physical characteristics. Journal of Geophysical Research 92 (C12):12947–12966.

LYVER, P. O., B. H. MOLLER, AND C. THOMPSON. 1999. Changes in Sooty Shearwater *Puffinus griseus* chick production and harvest precede ENSO events. Marine Ecology Progress Series 188:237–248.

MANTUA, N. J., S. R. HARE, Y. ZHANG, J. M. WALLACE, AND R. C. FRANCIS. 1997. A Pacific decadal climate oscillation with impacts on salmon. Bulletin of the American Meteorological Society 78:1069–1079.

MANUWAL, D. A., AND H. R. CARTER. 2001. Natural history of the Common Murre (*Uria aalge californica*). Pp. 1–32. *in* D. A. Manuwal, H. R. Carter, T. S. Zimmerman, and D. L. Orthmeyer (editors). Biology and conservation of the Common Murre in California, Oregon, Washington, and British Columbia. Volume 1: Natural history and population trends. U.S. Geological Survey, Information and Technology Report USGS/BRD/ITR-2000-0012. Washington, DC.

MANUWAL, D. A., AND A. C. THORESEN. 1993. Cassin's Auklet (*Ptychoramphus aleuticus*). *In* A. Poole, and F. Gill (editors). The Birds of North America, No. 50. The Academy of Natural Sciences, Philadelphia, PA, and the American Ornithologists' Union, Washington, DC.

MCCHESNEY, G. J., H. R. CARTER, AND D. L. WHITWORTH. 1995. Reoccupation and extension of southern breeding limits of Tufted Puffins and Rhinoceros Auklets in California. Colonial Waterbirds 18:79–90.

MCCRARY, M. D., D. E. PANZER, AND M. O. PIERSON. 2003. Oil and gas operations offshore California: status, risks, and safety. Marine Ornithology 31:43–49.

MCCULLAGH, P., AND J. A. NELDER. 1989. Generalized linear models, 2nd Edition. Chapman and Hall, London, UK.

MCGOWAN, J. A., D. CAYAN, AND R. L. M. DORMAN. 1998. Climate ocean variability and ecosystem response in the northeast Pacific. Science 281:210–217.

MCINTYRE, J. W., AND J. F. BARR. 1997. Common Loon (*Gavia immer*). *In* A. Poole, and F. Gill (editors). The Birds of North America, No. 313. The Academy of Natural Sciences, Philadelphia, PA, and the American Ornithologists' Union, Washington, DC.

MCIVER, W. R. 2002. Breeding phenology and reproductive success of Ashy Storm-Petrels (*Oceanodroma homochroa*) at Santa Cruz Island, California, 1995-98. M.S. thesis, Humboldt State University, Arcata, CA.

MINOBE, S. 1997. A 50–70 year climatic oscillation over the North Pacific and North America. Geophysical Research Letters 24:683–686.

MURRAY, K. G., K. WINNETT-MURRAY, Z. A. EPPLEY, G. L. HUNT, JR., AND D. B. SCHWARTZ. 1983. Breeding biology of the Xantus' Murrelet. Condor 85:12–21.

MURRAY, S. N., AND M. M. LITTLER. 1981. Biogeographical analysis of intertidal macrophyte floras of southern California. Journal Biogeography 8:339–351.

OEDEKOVEN, C. S., D. G. AINLEY, AND L. SPEAR. 2001. Variable responses of seabirds to change in marine climate: California Current, 1985-1994. Marine Ecology Progress Series 212:265–281.

PENNIMAN, T. M., M. C. COULTER, L. B. SPEAR, AND R. J. BOEKELHEIDE. 1990. Western Gull. Pp. 218–244 *in* D.G. Ainley, and R.J. Boekelheide (editors). Seabirds of the Farallon Islands: ecology, dynamics, and structure of an upwelling community. Stanford University Press, Palo Alto, CA.

PETERSON, W. T., AND F. B. SCHWING. 2003. A new climate regime in northeast Pacific ecosystems. Geophysical Research Letters 30(17), 1896, doi.10.1029/2003GL017528.

PIEROTTI, R. J., AND C. A. ANNETT. 1995. Western Gull (*Larus occidentalis*). *In* A. Poole, and F. Gill (editors). The Birds of North America, No. 174. The Academy of Natural Sciences, Philadelphia, PA, and the American Ornithologists' Union, Washington, DC.

PIERSON, M. O., M. D. MCCRARY, AND M. L. BONNELL. 2000. Seasonal abundance of coastal seabirds offshore Santa Barbara and Ventura Counties, California. Pp 428–434 *in* D. R. Browne, K. L. Mitchell, and H. W. Chaney (editors). Proceedings of the Fifth California Islands Symposium, Santa Barbara Museum of Natural History. Minerals Management Service, Camarillo, CA.

PITMAN, R. L., AND S. M. SPEICH. 1976. Black Storm-petrel breeds in the United States. Western Birds 7:71.

PORTER, J. M., AND S. G. SEALY. 1981. Dynamics of seabird multi-species feeding flocks: chronology of flocking in Barkley Sound, British Columbia, in 1979. Colonial Waterbirds 4:104–113.

RISEBROUGH, R. W. 1972. Effects of environmental pollutants upon animals other than man. Proceedings of Berkeley Symposium on Mathematical Statistics and Probability 6:443–463.

ROEMMICH, D. 1992. Ocean warming and sea level rise along the southwest U.S. coast. Science 257:373–375.

RUBEGA, M. A., D. SCHAMEL, AND D. M. TRACY. 2000. Red-necked Phalarope (*Phalaropus lobatus*). *In* A. Poole, and F. Gill (editors). The Birds of North America, No. 538. The Academy of Natural Sciences, Philadelphia, PA, and the American Ornithologists' Union, Washington, DC.

RUSSELL, R. W. 2002. Pacific Loon (*Gavia pacifica*). *In* A. Poole, and F. Gill (editors). The Birds of North America, No. 657. The Academy of Natural Sciences, Philadelphia, PA, and the American Ornithologists' Union, Washington, DC.

SAGARIN, R. D., J. P. BARRY, S. E. GILMAN, AND C. H. BAXTER. 1999. Climate-related change in an intertidal community over short and long time scales. Ecological Monographs 69:465–490.

SAS Institute Inc. 1999. SAS procedures guide. SAS Institute, Cary, NC.

SAVARD, J. L., D. BORDAGE, AND A. REED. 1998. Surf Scoter (*Melanitta perspicillata*). *In* A. Poole, and F. Gill (editors). The Birds of North America, No. 363. The Academy of Natural Sciences, Philadelphia, PA, and the American Ornithologists' Union, Washington, DC.

SCHIFF, K. C. 2000. Sediment chemistry on the mainland shelf of the Southern California Bight. Marine Pollution Bulletin 40:268–276.

SCHWING, F. B., S. J. BOGRAD, C. A. COLLINS, G. GAXIOLA-CASTRO, J. GARCIA, R. GOERICKE, J. GOMÉZ-VALDEZ, A. HUYER, K. D. HYRENBACH, P. M. KOSRO, B. E. LAVANIEGOS, R. J. LYNN, A. W. MANTYLA, M. D. OHMAN, W. T. PETERSON, R. L. SMITH, W. J. SYDEMAN, E. VENRICK, AND P. A. WHEELER. 2002. The state of the California Current, 2001–2002: will the California current system keep its cool, or is El Niño looming? California Cooperative Oceanic Fisheries Investigations Report 43:31–68.

SOWLS, A. L., A. R. DeGANGE, J. W. NELSON, AND G. S. LESTER. 1980. Catalog of California seabird colonies. USDI Fish and Wildlife Service, Biological Service Program, FWS/OBS 37/80. Washington, DC.

SPEAR, L. B., AND D. G. AINLEY. 1997. Flight speed of seabirds in relation to wind speed and direction. Ibis 139:234–251.

SPEAR, L. B., AND D. G. AINLEY. 1999. Migration routes of Sooty Shearwaters in the Pacific Ocean. Condor 101:205–218.

SPEICH, S. M., AND T. R. WAHL. 1989. Catalog of Washington seabird colonies. USDI Fish and Wildlife Service Biological Report. 88(6). Washington, DC.

STALLCUP, R. 1990. Ocean birds of the nearshore Pacific. Point Reyes Bird Observatory, Stinson Beach, CA.

STEPIEN, C. A., AND R. H. ROSENBLATT. 1991. Patterns of gene flow and genetic-divergence in the northeastern Pacific Clinidae, based on allozyme and morphological data. Copeia 1991:873–896.

STORER, R. W., AND G. L. NUECHTERLEIN. 1992. Western and Clark's grebes. *In* A. Poole, P. Stettenheim, and F. Gill (editors). The Birds of North America, No. 26. The Academy of Natural Sciences, Philadelphia, PA, and The American Ornithologists' Union, Washington, DC.

SYDEMAN, W. J., M. M. HESTER, J. A. THAYER, F. GRESS, P. MARTIN, AND J. BUFFA. 2001. Climate change, reproductive performance, and diet composition of marine birds in the southern California current system, 1969–1997. Progress in Oceanography 49: 309–329.

TAKEKAWA, J. E., H. R. CARTER, AND T. E. HARVEY. 1990. Decline of the Common Murre in central California, 1980–1986. Studies in Avian Biology 14:149–163.

U.S. CENSUS BUREAU. 2003. State and county quickfacts. <http://quickfacts.census.gov/qfd/states/06000.html> (23 August 2006).

U.S. COMMISSION ON OCEAN POLICY. 2004. An ocean blueprint for the 21st century. Washington, DC.

USDI FISH AND WILDLIFE SERVICE. 2002. Birds of conservation concern 2002. Division of Migratory Bird Management, Arlington, VA.

USDI FISH AND WILDLIFE SERVICE. 2005. Regional seabird conservation plan, Pacific Region. USDI Fish and Wildlife Service, Migratory Birds and Habitat Programs, Pacific Region, Portland, OR.

VEIT, R. R., J. A. McGOWAN, D. G. AINLEY, T. R. WAHL, AND P. PYLE. 1997. Apex marine predator declines ninety percent in association with changing oceanic climate. Global Change Biology 3:23–28.

VEIT, R. R., P. PYLE, AND J. A. McGOWAN. 1996. Ocean warming and long-term change in pelagic bird abundance within the California current system. Marine Ecology Progress Series 139:11–18.

VELARDE, E. 1999. Breeding biology of Heermann's Gulls on Isla Rasa, Gulf of California, Mexico. Auk 116:513–519.

WALLACE, E. A. H., AND G. E. WALLACE. 1998. Brandt's Cormorant (*Phalacrocorax penicillatus*). *In* A. Poole, and F. Gill (editors). The Birds of North America, No. 362. The Academy of Natural Sciences, Philadelphia, PA, and The American Ornithologists' Union, Washington, DC.

WARHAM, J. 1996. The behavior, population biology and physiology of the petrels. Academic Press, New York, NY.

WHITTOW, G. C. 1993a. Black-footed Albatross (*Diomedea nigripes*). *In* A. Poole, P. Stettenheim, and F. Gill (editors). The Birds of North America, No. 65. The Academy of Natural Sciences, Philadelphia, PA, and The American Ornithologists' Union, Washington, DC.

WHITTOW, G. C. 1993b. Laysan Albatross (*Diomedea immutabilis*). *In* A. Poole, P. Stettenheim, and F. Gill (editors). The Birds of North America, No. 66. The Academy of Natural Sciences, Philadelphia, PA, and The American Ornithologists' Union, Washington, DC.

WHITWORTH, D. L., H. R. CARTER, J. S. KOEPKE, R. J. YOUNG, F. GRESS, AND S. FANGMAN. In press.

Signs of recovery of Xantus's Murrelets after rat eradication at Anacapa Island, California. Marine Ornithology 33.

WHITWORTH, D. L., J. Y. TAKEKAWA, H. R. CARTER, S. H. NEWMAN, T. W. KEENEY, AND P. R. KELLY. 2000. At-sea distribution of Xantus's Murrelets (*Synthliboramphus hypoleucus*) in the Southern California Bight. Ibis 142:268–279.

WILBUR, S. R. 1987. Birds of Baja California. University of California Press, Berkeley, CA.

WINKLER, D. W. 1996. California Gull (*Larus californicus*). *In* A. Poole, and F. Gill (editors). The Birds of North America, No. 259. The Academy of Natural Sciences, Philadelphia, PA, and The American Ornithologists' Union, Washington, DC.